# MEN AND MOLECULES

# MEN
# AND
# MOLECULES

## by John F. Henahan

*Based on the radio series sponsored by the*
**AMERICAN CHEMICAL SOCIETY**

*Foreword by*
William J. Sparks, Ph.D.
*President, American Chemical Society*

*Introduction by*
Paul Saltman, Ph.D.

**Crown Publishers, Inc., New York**

# FOREWORD

In today's world there is scarcely a man—or woman or boy or girl—who is not directly affected by the advances of science. Of all the recognized scientific disciplines, chemistry is perhaps the most pervasive, for it touches nearly all areas of our lives and helps support other sciences with its discoveries. There is hardly a useful product or development that does not bear, somewhere, the imprint of chemical research. Hence any attempt to interpret the importance of chemistry should relate to other areas of science.

Accurate interpretation of science is becoming increasingly important in the modern world. Science is more than an extension of man's curiosity or a source of things for comfort and convenience; it is an important social force. Everyone needs to understand something of its scientific impact, and to have some idea of where chemistry stands in the scheme of things. And that is the principal value of this book.

*Men and Molecules* conveys much of the fascination and excitement of scientific research; furthermore, it reveals the motivations and procedures of scientists, the interdependence of the sciences, and the significance of chemistry for the course of human progress. Written for the alert layman, it will be valuable in increasing public understanding and in supplementing the study of science in high schools and colleges. It provides a thrilling account of the ways in which chemistry can be adapted to creating a world of better living. A major point made by the book is that chemists are seeking and finding answers to many of the enormous problems now confronting man: hunger, hereditary disease, mental illness, and the history and evolution of his own kind. The reader will find this book exciting and informative because it reveals in nonpedagogic fashion the background of important scientific discoveries of today, as well as the scientific explorations that may have a profound influence on the economic, social, and intellectual climate of tomorrow.

*Men and Molecules* is a considerable expansion of specific programs from the weekly radio science documentary of the same name, produced by the American Chemical Society for many years. Featuring distinguished researchers as they tell about their work and what it means to the public at large, it is one of the important ways in which the Society is fulfilling its obligation to foster public welfare by promoting public understanding of the importance of chemical research, both fundamental and applied.

The American Chemical Society, the world's largest organization devoted to a single scientific discipline, is the only society of this type that has a national charter from Congress.

The Society is placing increasing emphasis on its charter obligation "to encourage in the broadest and most liberal manner the advancement of chemistry in all its branches." To this end, the Society has taken cognizance of a growing governmental interest and activity in scientific areas, and therefore is trying to keep legislators and administrators in various government branches and agencies informed about matters involving chemistry. The Society supported the study by the Westheimer Committee of the National

Academy of Sciences, whose recent report underscored the need to keep both the public and those in government who are concerned with public welfare informed about chemists' contributions to the health, technology, and economics of our country. To facilitate the dissemination of such information and to broaden the Society's services to the government, the Society established last year a Committee on Chemistry and Public Affairs, headed by its former president, Professor Charles C. Price.

It is interesting to note that between 15 and 20 percent of federal income from taxes is spent on science-related research and development, which in itself behooves every citizen and taxpayer to be informed about the importance of chemical programs and the value of chemical progress. This book should serve an extremely useful purpose by providing some of this information to the public in intelligible, readable form.

WILLIAM J. SPARKS, Ph.D.
*President, American Chemical Society*

# PREFACE

Since the beginning of 1960, more than 500 scientists have found themselves at the open end of a microphone discussing their work and what it means or could mean to society. Although some eyed the tape recorder as warily as if it were capable of stealing their souls, most seemed pleased that someone was interested in atoms and molecules and their relationship to the world at large. The radio format that came out of these interviews took one direction, but it is the interview sessions that form the nucleus of this book.

Each chapter can be read without reference to another, but certain themes are clearly evident. If this book did not have its present name, it could very appropriately have carried the alternate title "Proteins and Nucleic Acids." These massive molecules appear in almost every chapter, always with new variations.

The enormous nucleic acid molecules which have been directing the code of life since it first appeared in the primordial soup are also entwined with the concept of molecular medicine, the war against viruses, new types

of insecticides, the fabrication of memory and the web a
spider weaves.

Proteins, which are of great scientific interest in trac-
ing the existence and evolution of anything that has ever
lived, are even more important to the protein-starved millions who are already threatened with malnutrition and
premature death.

It seems reasonable to retain the name "Men and
Molecules," because the two are inseparable in any consideration of the new frontiers of chemical research. Man
makes the molecules, tears them apart and puts them back
together again for the benefit of all. Man looks to his
own molecules for an understanding of his biochemical
machinery and for clues to the abnormal molecules that
harass his fellow man in the hospitals of the world. He
discovers a molecule that kills cattle, and then uses it to
keep men alive. The influence of molecules on man is so
all-pervasive that it is possible the simple process of reading this page may be making an imprint in the chemical
architecture of your brain cells.

In the preparation of the radio broadcasts that inspired
this book, scientists and interviewer got together anywhere there was room for today's portable equipment.
The field of operations encompassed the shady lawn of a
small New Hampshire college, the patio of a Florida
swimming pool, the cluttered basement of a government
building in Washington and countless laboratories. Because the interviews were held under field conditions,
listeners to the weekly broadcasts were not unaccustomed
to extraneous background sound: surf and sea gulls, miscellaneous laboratory blurps, whines and whistles, and
even the grind of a bulldozer noisily creating progress
outside a laboratory window. Fortunately it is easy to

purge these distractions from the printed page and it is hoped that the information contained herein comes through with a minimum of static.

Acknowledgments are certainly due to the many scientists who consented to interviews and took the time to check the manuscript for accuracy and context.

Thanks must also go to the more than 100,000 members of the American Chemical Society for making the "Men and Molecules" broadcasts possible. Kind sentiments are extended to Miss Catherine Ward who passed the manuscript through the keys of an electric typewriter and to the girl who made the index, my wife, Margaret. A pat on the head must also go to Sean, Jimmy, Bobby and Shivaun who went out to play "because Daddy is working."

J. F. H.

# ACKNOWLEDGMENTS

Grateful acknowledgment by the author is hereby made to the following for their contribution to this book: Bernard Agranoff, Mental Health Research Institute, University of Michigan; Aaron Altschul, United States Department of Agriculture Southern Regional Research Laboratories; Victor Auerbach, St. Christopher's Hospital for Children, Philadelphia, Pa.; Robert Baldridge, Temple University Medical School; Elso S. Barghoorn, Harvard University; D. John Bauer, Wellcome Laboratories of Tropical Medicine, London, England; Edward Bennett, University of California, Berkeley; Morton Beroza and Alexej Borkovec, USDA Research Laboratories, Beltsville, Md.; Harrison Brown, California Institute of Technology; Marvin Brunson, USDA Moorestown, N.J., Station; H. A. Campbell, Sloan-Kettering Memorial Institute; Paul Coleman, University of Maryland; Leon Coles, USDA Moorestown Station; Herbert Dessauer, Louisiana State University; J. Anthony Deutsch, New York University; Robert L. Fleischer, General Electric Research and Development Center; Sidney Fox, Institute for Molecular

Evolution, University of Miami, Fla.; Edward Geller, Veterans Administration Center, Los Angeles; Alvin J. Glasky, Abbott Laboratories; William D. Gray, Southern Illinois University; Robert Guthrie, State University of New York at Buffalo; A. M. Heimpel, USDA Research Laboratories, Beltsville, Md.; Thomas Hoering, Carnegie Institution, Washington, D.C.; C. M. Ignoffo, Bioferm Division, International Minerals and Chemical Corporation, Wasco, Calif.; Vernon Ingram, Massachusetts Institute of Technology; Alick Isaacs, National Institute for Medical Research, London, England; Martin Jacobson, USDA Research Laboratories, Beltsville, Md.; D. V. Josephson, Pennsylvania State University; Herbert E. Kaufmann, University of Florida, Gainesville; E. F. Knipling, USDA Research Laboratories, Beltsville, Md.; Richard Koch, Children's Hospital, Los Angeles; David Krech, University of California, Berkeley; L. S. Kucera, Mayo Clinic; Germain La Brecque, USDA Gainesville Laboratories; Bert La Du, New York University School of Medicine; Irving H. Leopold, Mount Sinai Hospital, New York City; E. P. Lichtenstein and Karl Paul Link, University of Wisconsin; Emanuel Margoliash, Abbott Laboratories; Rolland Mays, Linde Division, Union Carbide Corporation; Warren Meinschein, Indiana University; T. C. Merigan, Stanford University School of Medicine; R. M. Milton, Linde Division, Union Carbide Corporation; Claire C. Patterson, California Institute of Technology; Linus Pauling, Center for the Study of Democratic Institutions, Santa Barbara, Calif.; David Peakall, Upstate Medical Center, State University of New York; Lewis Petrinovich, State University of New York at Stony Brook; N. P. Plotnikoff, Abbott Laboratories; Cyril Ponnamperuma, Ames Research Center, NASA; P. Buford Price, General Electric Research and Development Center; Charles F.

# CONTENTS

# ILLUSTRATIONS

# INTRODUCTION

Science is a two-edged sword. The powerful meaning of Einstein's equation $E = mc^2$ can assume the shape of a mushroom cloud hovering over a firebomb of enormous destruction or it can represent controlled fission, locked within a power reactor, providing the energy for a civilization to move forward. Man's ability to produce antibiotic drugs capable of reducing or eliminating the communicable diseases induced by bacterial infection has, in large measure, been responsible also for the present population density of the earth. The technology of the internal-combustion engine threatens to choke urban society with its gaseous excreta, yet its real contribution to the well-being of man cannot be denied.

Everywhere we look on this planet, we see complex and profound problems in our society. A careful analysis of the basis of these difficulties shows that in some fundamental fashion science and technology are not only intimately involved but are also an integral part of the solution to these multiple sociological problems. Consider but a few examples: arms control and disarmament in a world faced with instantaneous nuclear holocaust; growth of population at a rate that doubles the number of human beings in the world every twenty years; the inability of two-thirds of the people who live on the earth today to secure a proper diet from the standpoint of total calories consumed as well as the proper balance of vitamins, proteins, and minerals; the migration of people to cities so that 70 percent of the population of the United States and Western Europe now exists in major metropolitan areas, creating myriad problems—of housing, transport, recreation, handling of waste, water, and so on; the ability to control the thoughts of man by the media of mass communication, by drugs, and by microelectrodes implanted in the brain.

The enormity of such problems and the absence of simple solutions cause most of us to throw up our hands in dismay and say, "Someone will make the decision for us"; or, "It's not for me; it's for the politicians to decide"; or, "Let the scientists worry about it; it's none of my doing." We take great pride in the democratic tradition in the United States, as do most of the people of Western Europe. It is the voice of the people that should be heard. It is the citizens' ideas, their concerns, their solutions that should guide the destinies of their government. But how can rational solutions to the problems outlined above be achieved when the overwhelming majority of the people of our nation are essentially ignorant of and alienated from science and technology? We are quick to seize upon the wonder drugs and praise them. We rush to the television tube to bask in the multilined electronic glow. We are ready to jump into high-powered automobiles, only to sit locked in the snarls of freeway jams. But this is not an appreciation of science and technology. It is in reality an abuse and desecration of them.

I think that there are three major reasons why our educated population is alienated from and by science. The greatest harm to a healthy attitude toward science is inflicted by the school systems. It begins in the elementary schools, intensifies in the high schools, and usually reaches its climax at the university level. This may seem a strange position for a university professor to take, but let me give you a few examples from my own experience to verify this hypothesis. One afternoon, our eight-year-old son returned from his third-grade class in elementary school delighted and enthusiastic over a lecture he had been given on how the telephone works. My first impression was that he had learned how sound waves are transformed into electromagnetic waves to be sent along a wire to be received, reconverted to sound, and thus permit communication over long distances. My initial hope was quickly dispelled when I asked him, "How, David?" and he replied, "You pick up the receiver, wait for the dial tone, and then carefully dial the number that you want." The lecture on telephone communication was not about how a telephone works, but how you work a telephone.

It is actually appalling to see the textbooks that are widely used in this country and abroad to communicate science to young minds thirsting to know and understand. Far too often, authors of textbooks fail to grasp the meaning of science. To me, science is a methodology by which man seeks to learn answers to such fundamental questions as How? Why? When? What? Science is a way of asking questions so that meaningful answers may be proposed. Thus it is a reasonable question to ask how many viruses can be placed on the head of a pin, but not how many angels may dance upon it. Science is a way of asking meaningful questions and proposing meaningful answers where the answers may be subjected to experimental testing and universal verification. It is quite obvious that the methodology of science is rarely introduced to the young student. Science becomes the memorization of parts of an animal, a cataloging of chemical elements and substances, a series of equations to be memorized and applied to meaningless problems. The student never senses the joy of personal discovery, never experiences the visceral pleasure of seeking and finding answers to his questions. It is only recently that programs of instruction have been developed in the primary schools to present an entirely new approach to the study of mathematics and the natural sciences. Perhaps ten years from today, children will not view science as a series of museum jars and problem sets.

Some effort has been expended at the high school level to develop new courses of study in the biological and physical sciences, particularly in chemistry. These approaches are to be lauded, but they are still in their infancy. Too often, the teachers of science complain of the complexity of the new programs. In fact, it has been my experience in talking with high school science teachers that they themselves feel alienated from modern science. It has got out of hand. A teacher without love for or understanding of his subject can instill little enthusiasm in his students. The National Science Foundation has made a very serious attempt to bring high school teachers into the universities during the summers to try to "rehabilitate" them to the happenings of the modern world of science. It has been estimated that the amount of scientific knowledge is doubling every seven years. Much of this has little bearing for the elementary or high school teacher, but a great deal of it must be appreciated and communicated. Only by means of summer programs or sabbatical years or in-group training can the public school teacher be kept intellectually alive and stimulated.

If a student survives elementary and high school education and still maintains an enthusiasm and love for science, it is oftentimes quickly crushed by university and college programs. There are few courses in the physical or biological sciences that I have encountered where science is presented in a dynamic and stimulating fashion. Not only are the lectures dull and dogmatic and the examinations a "contest" to prove the professor is smarter than the students; the labs are also a tedious series of cookbook exercises where known answers are unimaginatively found. Four years at college as an undergraduate chemistry major practically smothered all the joy and excitement I had experienced in high school science. In fact, if it hadn't been for a fortuitous set of circumstances involving one sympathetic professor and a trip to Paris for a year of biochemical research, I would have certainly walked away from science as a career.

Teachers have a fantastic responsibility to students. They must set the spark in the combustible kindling, then blow it into glowing coals, and ultimately into a burning fire of excitement within the pupil. Rigid curriculum be damned. It is time that scientists used a scientific approach to discover the most stimulating and effective ways of communicating.

Which brings up the second principal reason why people have been alienated from science. The practicing scientists by and large have withdrawn from their responsibility to communicate with the "other culture." They don't want to talk to nonscientists. They wish to communicate only with their peers. They have become so accustomed to the intricate language of their particular specialty that they find it requires a great deal of effort to rephrase their sentences to talk with the outsider. Even within science, a Tower of Babel has been erected so that the language of the strange particle physicist is not that of the quantum chemist, is not that of the molecular biologist, is not that of the geophysicist. We are threatened not only with these differences in language but also with the ever-expanding circumference of the scientific frontier. There are fewer generalists and more specialists. Each group fragments to subgroups, then to subsubgroups, and each subsubgroup with its own language meets in its own special small meetings while its members, with great delight, chat with one another but with no one else.

The pressures on contemporary scientists to produce new science are enormous. We have created a hierarchical structure involving both large sums of money—witness the multibillion-dollar grants and contracts of government—and peer-group prestige—the pecking order of the flock. Value judgments become clouded under these circumstances. Scientists will publish preliminary information long before it merits printer's ink on a white page. They do this because they know that publications "count" when new grants are sought or promotion to a higher rank within their university or a new job at another institution is desired. The fantastic ego drives of some scientists have led them to sins of commission as well as those of omission. Data have been faked and misinformation has been deliberately disseminated. Rarely is the scientist consumed by a driving ambition to be a great teacher.

Scientists have withdrawn from their obligation to communicate their knowledge to their students and to the nonscientific public. They have also deliberately avoided their responsibility to be intimately involved in governmental function. They have refused to stand up and to be heard and to be counted. Only recently have the national scientific societies and associations begun to recognize their intricate involvement with the machinery of government. Only recently have the scientists realized that they must look outward from their small subgroups and become responsible with their colleagues from all the intellectual disciplines for a cooperative effort in the attack upon ignorance.

A third and important contributing area to the lack of science appreciation by the public is the role—or better, the absence of a role—played by the mass media of communication. Numerous surveys of high school students have shown that the average teen-ager has a mental image of a scientist compounded from a Jerry Lewis–like absent-minded professor, a shaggy-haired sweat-shirted Albert Einstein, and a Dr. Science Evil extracted from a science-fiction horror movie. By and large, the media of television, radio, magazines, newspapers, and films have created a very unflattering image of the practicing scientist. In one survey it was found that over two-thirds of the girls in a high school would never consider marrying a scientist. Comic-book heroes wage relentless warfare against those pseudoscientific archcriminals who are using science and technology for their own evil ends.

When science is presented, it is usually in the idiom of the "Golly gee, Mr. Science, the light bulb turns on when you flip the switch!" It is *thing* science. It is blackboard and museum-jar science. It is pedagogy without love. There are moments of occasional brilliance where talents of the mass communicators are brought to bear—why should we consider the techniques used to sell toothpaste and soap beneath the dignity of the scientist and the teacher? I'm a great believer in putting "sex into science." We must not succumb to falsehood to sell our product or pitch that which is not true. But there is great excitement in what science has shown is true. There is so much action, if it could only get proper exposure.

There is a recent trend on the part of newspapers and national magazines to recruit top scientists to write in the idiom of the people. A fine chemist like Dr. Irving Benglesdorf fortunately has been seduced away from the bench to write a marvelous column relating the excitement of modern-day science to the real world. The number of men like him is growing, but we need many more. Dr. Isaac Asimov has wedded his talents as scholar, scientist, historian, and fictionalist to make great contributions to science communication.

The author of this book, John Henahan, is one of the new breed. As a member of the News Service staff of the American Chemical Society, he has seen and experienced and captured the excitement of chemistry. With a tape recorder, he has interviewed hundreds of scientists in their laboratories, at scientific meetings, and in their classrooms. He has been able to distill the essence of excitement from these men and women as they describe their discoveries. At the same time, John has recognized the two-edged sword of science and technology and has tried to inform the people, to get them vitally concerned. Every week, 460 stations broadcast his fifteen-minute radio program in the United States and abroad. From the transcripts of these programs prepared from the tapes, John has put together this wonderful volume of essays on contemporary scientific problems and their potential solutions. He has managed to leave the love in science. He has been able to capture some of the human glow that takes place in the laboratory the day the breakthrough comes. He has also been able to correlate these achievements with the important conflicts and paradoxes confronting society. I hope that the readers of this book will savor the joy of scientific discovery, begin to understand its methods and results and to build intellectual bridges between the two cultures. The ideas of the most modern scientific achievements can be understood if they are vividly presented and anxiously received.

PAUL SALTMAN, Ph.D.
University of Southern California

# MEN AND MOLECULES

# CHAPTER 1

## THE PROTEIN GAP

The world's population stands at three billion three hundred and eight million people. As present population trends continue to outstrip the most pessimistic expectations of population analysts, the number will more than double by the year 2000. The much discussed population explosion is already undergoing political, economic and military repercussions fed by the certainty of impending famine for millions.

In confronting the expected chaotic condition of thirty years from now, food planners find themselves beginning on the negative side of a ledger where the debits increase daily instead of getting smaller. Not only must something be done about the hundreds of millions who may be starving in 2000, but immediate attention must be directed to the half of the present world population that is now woefully undernourished.

As the population surges ahead in Asia, Africa and Latin America, diminishing food supplies will have to be distributed to more people unless something drastic and dramatic is done. Birth control is an obvious but not

1

universally accepted solution; however, even with population control, people must be fed well to survive. Much of the food that the underdeveloped areas now receive is nutritionally inadequate; it is either low in protein or lacks the kind of protein that the body needs to meet its uncompromising demands.

Dr. Aaron Altschul of the United States Department of Agriculture Southern Regional Research Laboratories in New Orleans recently indicated the seriousness with which he views the widening protein gap: "The only expression that is appropriate is that of being frightened. Not for the far future, but for this generation and the next."

Most underdeveloped areas rely on cereal protein derived from corn, wheat, rice, tapioca, etc., which is now being produced at the rate of a hundred million tons a year. Cereals contain about 10 percent protein, which is adequate to a point, but the cereal proteins lack certain essential amino acids found in meat, milk, eggs and fish protein. These nutritionally vital proteins are usually characterized as "animal proteins."

Nutritionists suggest that a normal adult male should receive about seventy grams of protein a day, with larger amounts going to pregnant women, children and the sick. Of the total protein requirement, about thirty grams should be of animal origin. However, only one quarter of the world's people receive more than thirty grams of animal protein daily; many receive far less. In India, animal protein consumption is an abysmal five grams a day, and the present total world deficit is about five million metric tons, one quarter of a year's total supply.

In Central and South America, as well as in the Dominican Republic, corn, or maize, is the cereal of choice. Although it is an excellent source of calories, it is a poor storehouse of essential animal protein. Out of this protein deficiency, a condition called kwashiorkor develops. Kwashiorkor is a Ghanian word meaning "first after second." It refers to the fact that it occurs when one child is taken from the breast and replaced by a second. Once the older child is removed from his mother's milk supply he goes into a steady decline which his normal corn-rich diet cannot reverse.

A child with kwashiorkor loses little weight, but he is very susceptible to cuts and bruises, poor bone development, enlarged liver, mental dysfunction and a premature death. In kwashiorkor areas, the peak death rate is sixty per thousand as compared to the mortality of four per thousand in other areas. Fortunately the condition can be quickly corrected if the child's diet is supplemented with essential animal protein.

Researchers all over the world have many ideas for keeping abreast and ultimately pulling ahead of the growing animal protein famine. Some of the more direct methods involve getting the most out of present food resources by making protein concentrates from fish and various high-protein seeds such as cottonseed and soybeans. Other more exotic approaches are to molds, fungi, bacteria and even the oil fields as rich protein factories for the world's future billions. However, most scientists warn that any really startling success hinges on making affected populations aware of their own nutritional plight, then teaching them how to correct it.

Protein resources now available could put the present population on a much-improved nutritional footing if they were utilized as they should be, many experts point out. Unfortunately, in many areas where the protein gap is widest, the available animal protein is being wasted or misdirected in one way or another.

For example, food researchers believe that if the unmatched animal protein resources of the sea could be converted into protein concentrates, i.e., fish meal or fish flour, nutritional deficiencies could be erased in a very short time. Idealistic though this viewpoint may be, it is often frustrated by the sobering realities of national economics and world trade.

Peru, a country which is severely lacking in animal protein, has, at the same time, a thriving fish meal industry which produces more than a million tons of nutritious fish meal annually. What frustrates the food experts is that almost the entire output of fish meal—derived from anchovies, incidentally—is exported to North America, where it is used in poultry feed.

Here Peru has the choice of a rich market for animal feed in North America or the production of fish protein concentrates for its own consumption. For the moment the input of dollars seems more important than the input of animal protein. Sizing up the economic facts of life as they now exist, Dr. J. A. Lovern of the Torry Research Station in Aberdeen, Scotland, told an American Chemical Society symposium on World Protein Resources: "If fish protein concentrate production (for human use) becomes a major industry in such countries as Peru, there will be repercussions in the animal feedstuffs industry, mainly affecting the presently affluent and well-fed countries, most of which are big importers of fish meal."

Incongruities between protein malnutrition and actual protein resources are again demonstrated in India where the streets and countryside are jammed with potentially rich, but relatively unused, protein producers. In a country where there are 220 million cattle for a 440 million population, most of the animals are used as beasts of burden or very inefficient milk suppliers. In India, starvation is literally a sacred cow; religious beliefs prevent the slaughter of cattle, and people go hungry.

Aside from the fact that cows are not eaten, the milk they produce does little to bridge the animal protein gap. India produces 48.5 billion pounds of milk a year, which measures out to about five ounces a day for every person. (In the United States, average milk consumption is about a quart a day per person.) Sixty percent of India's milk production is converted into a rancid butterfat preparation called ghee, which is eaten with enthusiasm by the population. But in its preparation, most of its protein has been destroyed.

As an inkling of how much milk protein is *not* getting to the consumer in India, consider dairy production statistics in the United States. In 1945, 27.7 million cows yielded about 120 billion pounds of milk a year. Twenty years later, there were only 17.6 million cows, but they *increased* total milk production to 127 billion pounds, thanks to intelligent breeding, feeding and excellent dairy management. In fact, average milk production per cow has increased from a very respectable 5,880 pounds a year to a phenomenal 7,880 pounds.

### PROTEIN ON THE HOOF

As valuable as animal protein is, livestock are relatively inefficient protein-making machines. For example, only 23 percent of the protein that a cow takes in ends up as usable protein in its meat or milk. Beef cattle pay back about

10 percent of their protein intake, while pigs return 12 percent.

The low turnover rate has caused many researchers to wonder whether or not man will be able to continue using his precious acreage to grow forage and grain for animals when he might better use it himself. Others insist that man is not going to give up animal agriculture very easily and that its protein potential is far from being realized at the present time.

Dairy chemists, including Dr. D. V. Josephson of Pennsylvania State University, think that the peculiar four-part stomach arrangement of the cow and other ruminants such as sheep and goats might be a natural way of making good milk protein without sacrificing agricultural acreage. The first stomach, or rumen, digests the animal's food, and transforms it into nutritious proteins. Unlike other animals, the ruminant's stomach has no enzymes for digestion and must rely on the activities of billions and billions of bacteria to break down its food. Chemists feel that the cow probably does not need a very rich protein diet to make milk and that the versatile bacteria in her first stomach compartment might be able to get by with much less valuable foodstuffs.

One possibility, says the Penn State researcher, would be to feed the cow whey, a cheese by-product produced to no real purpose in the United States at the rate of fifteen billion pounds a year. In the Penn State laboratories, chemists have developed a high nitrogen cattle feed by fermenting whey, then treating it with ammonia gas. According to Dr. Josephson, when ruminants are fed the material, they do not enjoy it as much as conventional feed, but they remain healthy and are very satisfactory milk producers.

Earlier, Dr. A. I. Virtanen, the Finnish Nobel Laureate in Chemistry, fed cows on a completely synthetic diet consisting of starch, sucrose, cellulose, urea, corn oil, various ammonium salts and small amounts of Vitamins A and D. Although the cows produced only about 4,500 pounds of milk a year (about half the output of high milk producers), Dr. Virtanen's point was proved: the cow's diet contained no protein at all, she lived a normal life, kept up her weight and produced calves just like other cows on a normal diet.

According to the Finnish chemist, his earlier studies might pave the way for even simpler diets: "If a cheap, sufficiently digestible carbohydrate feed can be prepared from straw, wood, sugar cane waste or other fast-growing plants, or even synthetically, it may be possible by milk production to remove protein and vitamin deficiency in vast areas inhabited by undernourished peoples."

As was suggested earlier, many people are not able to drink as much milk as they need for a number of reasons, ranging from religious taboos to tribal custom. In areas where cattle are raised primarily as a prestige item, the milk is fed to calves in preference to the members of the community. Researchers of the United Nations Food and Agricultural Organization (FAO) find that it takes at least twenty milking cows to supply enough milk for one nomadic family. Neither is there any incentive for native farmers to market the milk that their cattle might produce. There are no central processing plants, essentially no refrigeration and no distribution centers to get it to the people who need it.

FAO experts note that when they are able to convince a farmer that his cows would produce more milk through breeding and improved agricultural practices, he may become discouraged when he discovers that no one wants the milk his cows produce. He finds it much easier and more profitable to sell the cream, with its high butterfat content, and pays less attention to marketing the skim milk with its much more vital animal protein.

Attacking the distribution problem directly, FAO and UNICEF have set up a number of rural cooperative milk processing centers in Kenya where the discrepancy between the number of cows and milk production is especially acute. When the Diesel-powered plants were first set up in the Kenyan countryside, about twelve gallons of milk were brought in each day for processing. Two years later, each plant was processing about 1,000 gallons a day, says FAO's Dr. Isaac Mann.

Encouraging as the FAO results were, it is unlikely that the processing plants will solve the milk protein problem in the near future. To provide even a half pint of milk a day for the one billion people now grossly underfed, 2,500 new processing plants, each with a 100,000-liter-a-day capacity would have to be built immediately. To feed the expected population of a decade hence, it is estimated that one new plant would have to be opened every day of the year for the next ten years to catch up with the world's expected milk protein deficiency.

SEED PROTEIN CONCENTRATES

Readily available, but relatively untapped, food sources, whose protein content can be favorably compared to animal protein, are the oil seeds, such as soybean, peanuts and cottonseed. Potentially these seeds could contribute an additional twenty million tons of protein to the expanding population, but except for soybean, very little reaches human stomachs in the critically underfed areas.

The USDA's Dr. Altschul has remarked that "if all the protein of just the cottonseed, peanuts and soybean now grown were made available as a concentrate for human consumption, this would have the effect of doubling the quantity of protein concentrates now available. This alone ought to wipe out the world protein concentrate deficit that now exists."

The value of soybean protein has been recognized for more than fifty centuries in the Orient where soybean curd (tofu) and a fermented soybean preparation (tempeh) have helped soften the impact of the protein deficiency that usually occurs in poorly developed areas.

Soybean milk, a by-product of tofu production, is now a big seller in Hong Kong where it is drunk with gusto by adults and children. However, because it must be prepared in carefully supervised plants and refrigerated like cow's milk, the nutritious soybean milk seldom reaches the hinterlands. In fact, the lack of efficient, sanitary and economical seed-processing plants is viewed by many experts as one of the chief obstacles to more widespread use of the milk.

The United States, which is the largest soybean producer in the world (over 800 million bushels annually), finds a good market for soybean protein concentrates as animal feed, while soybean oil is now considered a surplus product eligible for distribution to other countries as part of the government's Food for Peace program. However, the oil does little to plug the protein gap because it contains none of that vital commodity. American soybean producers also sell unprocessed soybeans to West

Germany and Japan, although these countries have no protein problem at present. Going to the other extreme, very little soybean is produced in protein-starved India.

As United States soybean production increased, American growers inspired an international interest in getting the maximum food value out of the soybean crop. A twenty-five-year-old American process produced edible soybean meal or grits containing 50 percent or more of high-quality protein. This relatively cheap process combined heat and solvent extraction techniques to remove fat and deleterious substances from the soybean without destroying one of its most valuable amino acids—lysine. One shortcoming is the slightly bitter taste that results from the heat process which has blocked popular acceptance of the soybean products throughout the world.

Dr. Max Milner of UNICEF estimates that "if the present United States soybean crop were to be processed entirely into such toasted soybean products . . . it could provide 750 million children with a forty-gram portion of high-quality protein a day."

More recently, advocates of soybean protein concentrates have been very encouraged by a "full-fat soy flour" developed in a cooperative project with UNICEF by scientists of the USDA's Northern Utilization Research and Development Division in Peoria, Illinois, and the Wenger Mixer Manufacturing Company.

As the name suggests, the flour contains both soybean oil and soybean protein, which could make it very useful in areas where both calories and protein are in short supply. The flour is said to have a good taste, it can be stored for long periods of time, and is nutritionally adequate for young children. It can be used alone, in beverages such as soy milk and baby's formula, or with cereal products in macaroni, noodles, baked goods and soups. One of the big practical advantages of the full-fat soy flour is that it can be produced continuously on a small scale, which puts it in easy reach of countries that cannot afford to build large-scale production plants. According to UNICEF's Dr. Milner, who was instrumental in getting the full-fat soy flour project under way, "This approach to edible soybean processing, particularly in terms of providing low-cost foods in developing countries, seems to represent a major technological advance."

Among the oil seed crops, cottonseed ranks next to soybean in volume production, but it has the added advantage of being produced in the protein-poor areas of India, Central and South America and Africa. In spite of this, cottonseed has traditionally been considered either as a useless leftover from cotton production or as a source of protein-free cottonseed oil. Until recently the protein-rich seed cake has been considered unfit even for animal consumption; in India it is used primarily as fertilizer.

In the United States, much of the cottonseed protein goes for the feeding of cows and other livestock whose versatile first stomachs can handle the cottonseed feeds, but there are other reasons why it has not been used to help solve the world's protein problem. One of these is that the seed contains gossypol, a poisonous dye, which researchers have only recently learned how to remove without destroying useful protein. Secondly, archaic and inadequate processing techniques in India and other nutritionally underdeveloped areas are primarily aimed at salvaging the cottonseed oil instead of the residual press cake that contains the protein.

In spite of the earlier obstacles to its widespread use, cottonseed is now one of the liveliest contenders in the seed protein concentrate area. In Central America, children suffering with the advanced stages of kwashiorkor were cured when their daily diet of corn was supplemented with an all-vegetable mixture called Incaparina.

Developed at the Institute of Nutrition in Central America and Panama, in cooperation with North American researchers, the lifesaving preparation contains corn flour, sorghum, yeast, Vitamin A and most importantly, 38 percent of a cottonseed protein concentrate. Since its introduction in 1961, Incaparina has become established in Central America and has reached an annual production of about two million pounds in Guatemala and Colombia.

New cottonseed processes developed by researchers in the USDA's Southern Regional Laboratory in New Orleans, as well as in Sicily and India, can produce high protein concentrates containing little or none of the poisonous pigment gossypol. All of the processes use a variety of chemical solvents including acetone, hexane and water, to sidestep the need for protein-destroying heat which was used in earlier processes.

Recently, plant geneticists made a contribution to solving the food protein problem by developing varieties of cottonseed that contain no gossypol. Fortuitously, the new cottonseed breeding factor can be introduced into all strains of cottonseed, and the National Cottonseed Producers Association hopes to make the new varieties available on a large scale by 1970. Present protein flours produced from the gossypol-free seeds are lighter colored than other cottonseed flours and meet high nutritional standards.

### PROTEIN FROM THE SEA

In 1963, the world fish catch was 46.4 million metric tons of which about three-fourths went to the human food market. Because the figure represents only a small fraction of the theoretical seafood potential, food planners are logically looking at the world's oceans, rivers and streams for help in closing the protein gap.

Much attention has been given to "fish flours" or meals containing more protein on a weight basis than the original fish did, but as you read earlier, these valuable protein concentrates often bypass the dinner table and are fed to animals. Because the fish protein concentrates are made from the entire fish, they are prone to contamination by harmful bacteria, which has led some governments to block their use by humans. Also fish flours, especially those made from oily fish varieties, tend to get rancid very quickly when exposed to the air. As discovered in a number of feeding studies, rancid fish fats can destroy useful vitamins when they are eaten for a long period of time, which at least partially negates any protein value they might have.

Some fish-meal producers thwart the formation of the rancid oils by adding commercial antioxidants to the fish protein concentrate as soon as it leaves the drier. However, in a number of countries which have restrictions against the use of chemical antioxidants in foodstuffs, such fish meals and flours are probably out of the question.

Recently FAO experts became very interested in non-rancid fish meal made in Ghana from a local sardine that appears to contain a natural antioxidant, called tocopherol. Since the discovery of the sardine, which was at first received very skeptically by scientists, British researchers report that the sprat, a herring relative caught off the English coast, also contains large amounts of tocopherol and can be made into a fish flour that does not "go sour."

The United States Department of the Interior's Bureau

of Commercial Fisheries recently announced a new process for producing a "clinically pure" fish concentrate containing 80 percent protein. The Department's experts estimate that if the unharvested fish now running in American waters were converted into such a fish flour, it would meet the protein requirements of one billion persons for three hundred days.

The new fish flour has already been approved as "safe for human consumption" by scientists from the National Academy of Sciences and the National Research Foundation who were contracted by the government to evaluate its production costs and possible toxicity. In 1962, the Food and Drug Administration, which passes on the safety of food products eaten in the United States, turned down an earlier fish flour, on the grounds that the flour was "polluted and filthy." Although this view was disputed by some scientists, the judgment served to create a bad reputation for fish protein concentrate in general.

In the new American fish flour process, the whole fish, including head, tail, fins and entrails, is ground to a pulp, then bathed in cold isopropyl alcohol. This "rubbing alcohol" treatment, which removes most of the water and fish fat, is followed by two more hot alcohol baths, to eliminate all other traces of fats and contaminants. When spray-dried, the end product is an off-white flour containing beneficial minerals and the previously mentioned 80 percent protein.

The government's team of advisers concluded that the fish flour could be produced to sell anywhere from 13 to 18 cents a pound, depending on the size of the producing plant. This would mean that a three-year-old child could get his entire animal protein requirement from about a half ounce of fish concentrate for about a half penny a day. Even with distribution and retailing expenses added in, the ration would cost no more than three cents a day, say FAO experts. It seems likely that high-quality animal protein at such a low price would be extremely welcome in areas where meat, eggs and fresh milk are unavailable or too expensive.

### PROTEIN ON THE RESEARCH HORIZON

There are now more than 100,000 different types of tiny protein-producing plants that are almost completely ignored as food staples. These unused protein suppliers are the fungi, which include the yeasts, mushrooms and molds.

Currently none of the fungi have made any impact on the world's expanding protein requirements; in fact, only one mushroom type out of several hundred edible varieties is being produced commerically in the United States for human consumption.

Dr. William D. Gray, professor of botany at Southern Illinois University in Carbondale, maintains that not only could fungi meet the imminent protein famine in Africa, Asia and Latin America, but they could also be fed to animals in this country when the growing urban civilization cuts even more deeply into the available crop acreage.

Unlike green plants, fungi cannot photosynthesize; that is, they cannot produce sugar for their own growth from carbon dioxide, sunlight and water; they must be fed from some source of carbon and hydrogen. Carbohydrates, such as the sugar glucose, are among the most efficient carbon sources. In any large-scale culture of fungus, refined sugar would probably be too expensive as a carbon source, but fortunately there are many carbo-hydrate-containing plants that can be used as food for the fungus. These are the plants, incidentally, which are used in low-protein areas of the world.

To Dr. Gray this means that if these plants were "fed" to fungi, they could economically produce much more protein than they would ever supply if eaten directly. Even better, by acting as biochemical middlemen for the fungi, they would help manufacture a protein food much richer than either could produce separately.

Using a group of microorganisms known as *Fungi Imperfecti,* Dr. Gray has been very successful in con-verting plant carbohydrate into fungal protein in his laboratory. To begin, he minces or grinds up the plants and suspends them in water, along with a few mineral salts. Then he adds the fungus itself, bubbles in some air, and stirs the entire mixture for up to four days. The end product, which looks a little like tapioca, takes the form of off-white pellets and is virtually odorless and tasteless when dried, says Dr. Gray.

Large areas of the tropical and subtropical world rely on a vegetable called manioc as their main food staple. It is a long fleshy root that resembles a white sweet potato. Although manioc is rich in carbohydrates (32 per cent) it contains only 0.7 percent protein. At that rate, a person would have to eat about twenty-five pounds of manioc a day to meet his daily protein needs.

Based on world production figures for manioc, Dr. Gray estimates that the fungal conversion technique could make enough protein to supply the total annual protein requirements for an additional 145 million people. This figure is based on present tropical agricultural methods which could easily be made three times more efficient than they now are, he believes. At maximum production levels, fungal protein produced through the manioc middleman could theoretically nourish an additional 434 million people.

If rice were fed to the fungal protein factory, it would go much further than manioc could in paring away the world's protein shortage, says Dr. Gray. Because rice contains 7.5 percent protein, as well as 70 percent carbohydrate, the fungal conversion method could yield more than 48 billion pounds of crude protein—enough to meet the annual needs of 1.743 billion people, more than half the world's present population. Again, these figures are based on rice production statistics which could also be increased significantly by improved rice cultivation methods, according to Dr. Gray.

Based on laboratory studies, the botanist believes that many other carbohydrate crops could help wipe away the current protein deficit. These include white potatoes, sweet potatoes, sugar beets, cassava flour, corn, citrus, molasses, beet molasses and blackstrap molasses. In fact, he notes, even wood pulp has been a fair starting material for the protein-manufacturing machinery of the *Fungi Imperfecti*.

Dr. Gray has calculated that if only seven major crops were converted into fungal protein, the protein would meet the yearly needs of more than four and one half billion people.

At the present time, very little is known about the nutritional worth of fungal proteins, although short-term feeding trials with mice indicate that they gain weight as rapidly as mice fed on a standard mouse diet.

"In view of the vast numbers of species and strains of

## Protein that could theoretically be produced by conversion of carbohydrate crops into fungal protein

| Crop | World Production in Millions of Tons 1962–1963 | Percent of Protein in Crops | Total Crop Protein in Billions of Pounds | Total Protein* in Billions of Pounds From Fungal Conversion | Millions of People Whose Protein Needs Could Be Satisfied |
|---|---|---|---|---|---|
| Manioc | 84.600 | 0.7 | 1.184 | 7.952 | 152 |
| Sugar Beet | 288.000 | 0.75 | 4.320 | 15.840 | 305 |
| Sugar Cane | 480.000 | Negligible | Negligible | 14.400 | 276 |
| Rice | 277.088 | 7.5 | 41.5632 | 90.0532 | 1,725 |
| Corn | 243.600 | 7.0 | 34.094 | 70.624 | 1,350 |
| Yams and Sweet Potatoes | 130.704 | 1.8 | 4.705 | 13.854 | 265 |
| White Potatoes | 294.324 | 2.0 | 11.772 | 25.829 | 494 |
| Total | 1,798.316 | | 97.6382 | 238.5522 | 4,567 |

* The total protein figures include the protein contained in the original crop plus the amount theoretically produced by the fungus.

*Fungi Imperfecti* that exist, it would seem that this is a very fruitful area to explore," Dr. Gray told the ACS World Protein Symposium. "It is not suggested that by themselves the fungi will solve all of the world's protein needs; however, it is time that some of the myths be dispelled and we begin to have a much closer look at a group of living organisms which appear to have a real potential in the area of protein synthesis."

Petroleum engineers have long been plagued by bacterial nuisances that thrive in the bottom of oil storage tanks and oil-water separators in refineries. As a result they have had to devote thousands of hours of research thinking to eliminate the oil-hungry microorganisms. Road builders also have their share of problems with bothersome bacteria that literally "eat up the road" as they feed on the bituminous undercoating of the nation's highways.

In spite of the bacteria's bad reputation, oil chemists and nutritionists anticipate that someday they might be able to put these pests to work as valuable protein producers. The bacteria use the petroleum hydrocarbons as a source of carbon, which they build into protein for their own use. Several petroleum researchers have become interested enough in this phenomenon to set up pilot plants to see whether the world's vast oil resources might help brighten its protein future.

Dr. Alfred Champagnat of Société Française des Pétroles, B.P. (British Petroleum), believes that bacteria are much better animal protein producers than beef cattle are. Grazing in a pasture, a 1,000-pound cow turns the grass into edible protein at the rate of about a pound a day. The same weight of bacterial microorganisms, feeding on certain petroleum hydrocarbons, produces 2,750 pounds of protein in the same "grazing" day. Bacteria are also less demanding than cows; they do not care what the weather is and do not need as much personal attention as cows do.

Dr. Champagnat also calculates that if petroleum were used as a protein source, it would make only a small dent in current oil reserves. If the petroleum-derived protein were produced at the rate of 20 million tons a year, the bacteria would use up about 40 million tons of crude oil a year, only about 3 percent of total oil production in an average year.

In the Pétroles B.P. pilot plant at Lavéra, French researchers have been experimenting with mixtures of different petroleum hydrocarbons to determine which varieties will produce the largest amount and the most nutritious protein product. Using ammonia (very available in the petroleum industry) as a nitrogen source and a stream of air for oxygen, the pilot plant has produced as much as a pound of yeastlike microorganisms from each pound of petroleum hydrocarbons used. The yeast contains about 50 percent animal protein, says Dr. Champagnat, and appears to be very digestible and nutritious in preliminary feeding tests with rats. Fortunately the protein is high in lysine, an amino acid which is usually very deficient in cereal crops. For that reason, it might first be used to supplement cereals in protein-deficient areas. Like Dr. Gray's fungal protein, the petroleum-originated protein is an off-white solid which can be fabricated into chewy gels and given a meat or fish flavor to suit the palates of a given area.

Researchers at the United States Bureau of Mines have also been feeding one of nature's ample fuel staples to microorganisms in the hope of getting usable protein in return. Early reports from the Bureau's Pittsburgh laboratories suggest that when four common soil yeasts fed on certain coal chemicals, the microbes obliged with moderate yields of cellular material that could be converted into a dry, whitish protein flour.

Also taking advantage of the microbes' appetite for petroleum hydrocarbons are scientists at the Institute of Gas Technology in Chicago, who have found that natural gas, when fed to certain strains of bacteria, is an excellent source of cellular material. IGT's Dr. Bernard Wolnak says that small-scale studies show that the end product contains from 35 to 40 percent protein, including the essential amino acids lysine, methionine and tryptophane. In addition, the bacterial cells contained relatively large amounts of Vitamin B-12, which is used widely as a nutritional supplement.

### THE REAL HOPE

Although most of the protein-building ideas discussed in this chapter are still in the experimental stage, many highly developed countries are exporting sizable amounts of wheat and other commodities to areas where local crops cannot feed the population. In addition, the United States sends a nonfat dry milk preparation overseas, fortified with Vitamins A and D. When reconstituted with water, the milk meets the minimum protein needs of men, women and children who hardly ever encounter animal protein in their daily diets.

The realization that increased food production in general will necessarily put future populations in a better protein condition than they are now has led some experts to suggest that massive amounts of chemical fertilizers—purchased by or distributed to countries as foreign aid—might help avert the gigantic famine almost certain to sweep through Asia, Africa and Latin America by 1970.

Observing that "fertilizer offers the best possibility of a substantial increase in agricultural production between now and 1980," Dr. Raymond Ewell of the State University of New York in Buffalo warns: "Historians of the future may remark on whether it was more important to have worked toward putting a man on the moon during the 1960's or to have worked toward averting the world famine of the 1970's.

"The problem is how can the countries of Asia, Africa and Latin America obtain a supply of (an estimated) fifteen million tons of plant nutrients by 1970 and thirty million tons by 1980. Domestic production of fertilizer in all these continents was about 1.5 million tons in 1963–64 and a good estimate for 1970 production would be three to four million tons. Production in 1970 might be increased to five to six million tons by a crash program of fertilizer plant construction, but generally speaking it is already too late to increase production greatly in 1970. Therefore it appears to me that most of the fertilizer needed by Asia, Africa and Latin America will have to be imported from the industrialized countries."

For the longer run, that is, in the world beyond 1980, countries will be able to get the most out of their available acreage only by producing fertilizer within their own borders. But even then, says Dr. Ewell, charity doled out by better-off countries will play a major part in assuring the survival of millions of starving people.

He predicts: "The fertilizer and fertilizer plants needed

by the countries of Asia, Africa and Latin America will largely have to come from the industrialized countries including the United States, Canada, Western Europe, Eastern Europe, the Soviet Union and Japan. In fact they will have to be largely given to these countries for the simple reason that they don't have any money."

As uplifting as charity may be for the donor, most food experts agree that the expected world famine can be averted only through drastic birth-control measures and a strong will on the part of the affected countries to solve their own food problems. However, the problem is compounded by the fact that even when a man is starving, and knows the reasons for it, he is still particular about what he eats. A man may agree that a protein concentrate from fish, soybean or some other source will do him good, but he is still at the mercy of culinary traditions that stretch back to the beginnings of his civilization. If he has a choice between a handful of rice and a suspicious-looking powder, he will probably choose the bowl of rice and hope it gets him through another day. Even though it is now possible to fabricate protein concentrates that look and taste like meat and fish, nutritionists continually struggle with the ingrained reluctance to try something new.

All of the above suggests that science is not necessarily the ultimate answer to worldwide protein deficiency. A large part of the problem is breaking down centuries-old food prejudices, irrational taboos, fads and fallacies that contribute to mankind's self-starvation.

The consensus of the men who wrestle with the spectre of a protein famine is that nations must learn or be taught that good nutrition is vital, and certainly not cheap, even in Utopian societies. They must realize the seriousness of their situation and that adequate nutrition, although costly, is far less costly to a nation's growth than the lives of millions who will die unaware that the problem can be solved.

Speaking of the milk-production problem, Dr. D. V. Josephson expresses sentiments that can probably be applied to the world protein situation in general:

"It is generally recognized that the dairy industry in the less developed nations must literally emerge from the grass roots and that the mere acquisition of a knowledge of the technology of cattle management, feed and pasture production is not enough. The knowledge must be conveyed to the peasant.

"In most of these countries where the majority of cattle owners are illiterate and the more enlightened have little more than four to five years of schooling, the problem becomes a real challenge. Programs are now emerging in which formal and informal training is being accomplished through such elementary techniques as word of mouth, reading, memorizing, watching and doing under supervision. It is a monumental task but a necessary one.

"An oft-quoted ancient Chinese proverb may well be the key to the problem of providing a more adequate supply of protein around the world. It goes, 'Give a man a fish and he will eat for a day. Teach him to fish, and he will eat for the rest of his life.' "

# CHAPTER 2

## MOLECULAR MEDICINE

Less than a century ago, tuberculosis, diphtheria and malaria were deadly and seemingly invincible enemies of mankind. Now each of these diseases, caused by some bacterium or virus, is on the wane; complete control is a future possibility if not a current reality.

As medical researchers and physicians become increasingly adept at treating these germ-caused diseases, they are finding more time to study and combat other diseases, which are, in effect, part of man's heritage. In fact, as the more familiar diseases decline, the so-called genetic diseases—inborn errors of metabolism—are showing at least a relative surge upward.

Unless he has been touched by such hereditary diseases, the average person has never heard of most of them. Names such as Tay-Sachs disease, Wilson's disease, sickle-cell anemia, do not ring the same mental bell as mumps or chicken pox do. Other hereditary diseases whose names reflect their biochemical roots, such as phenylketonuria, galactosemia and histidinemia mean even less.

As scientists become more familiar with the chemistry of the genes—those tiny packets of hereditary information that we all carry around with us in every cell—they find themselves on the threshhold of eliminating these malevolent remnants of man's evolution. A new field of study is emerging, a field dubbed "molecular medicine" by the distinguished chemist Linus Pauling. Professor Pauling won the Nobel Prize for Chemistry in 1953, and in 1964 he became the first man to receive a second Nobel award, when he won the Peace Prize.

Each of us represents the product of a genetic equation which usually works with mathematical certainty to our advantage, but which can occasionally cause trouble. Chemical factors in the genes which are passed from parent to offspring determine whether the resulting equation reads favorably or unfavorably. Normally the genes provide hereditary information that guides the manufacture of the proteins—found in every cell, tissue and organ of the body. Of all the proteins, hemoglobin is among the most important.

Hemoglobin, a substance found in the red blood cells, carries oxygen to all the organs of the body. Thus, it means life to all of us. Currently there are more than a dozen abnormal hemoglobin conditions known, each of which results from some defect in the genetic machinery. In 1949, Professor Pauling and his co-workers at the California Institute of Technology began to map out the molecular basis of one of the most serious hemoglobin abnormalities—sickle-cell anemia.

No one knows exactly when sickle-cell anemia originated in Africa, but thousands of Negroes are born with the disease every year. The fate of a child suffering from the disease or its complications is extremely unpleasant, as a catalog of typical symptoms shows: A victim of sickle-cell anemia may suffer weakness, general lassitude, poor physical development, rheumatism from muscle and joint damage, pneumonia as a result of lung damage, kidney failure and enlargement of the spleen.

Sickle-cell anemia is found in either sex and is transmitted by what is known as an autosomal recessive gene. This means that each sickle-cell anemia sufferer has inherited *two* genes—one from each of his parents—that direct the manufacture of the abnormal hemoglobin molecule. Once that genetic message is given, the biochemical switch is always "on," grinding out more abnormal hemoglobin every day until eventually the victim dies. On the other hand, a child who inherits only one sickle-cell gene has another gene that makes normal hemoglobin, giving him an approximately fifty-fifty mixture of the two types of hemoglobin in his blood. A child with one sickle-cell gene is said to carry the sickle trait and to have sicklemia. He can lead a relatively normal life, but he has one serious disadvantage. If he goes to high altitudes where the oxygen in the air is thin, he can become seriously ill or die. For him, one trip in an unpressurized airplane could be fatal. The single gene has a side advantage in areas where malaria is prevalent, as will be discussed later.

Linus Pauling's interest in sickle-cell anemia was first aroused in 1948 when he heard a talk by Dr. William B. Castle, a physician at the Thorndyke Laboratory of Boston City Hospital. As Professor Pauling remembers it:

"Dr. Castle was talking about patients with sickle-cell anemia, and he said that their red blood cells were twisted out of shape. He added that the spleen destroys these twisted red cells—which it recognizes as being abnormal. It destroys them so rapidly, in fact, that the patient can not manufacture new red cells fast enough to keep himself in good health. He has a severe anemia."

Professor Pauling admits that he was listening to Dr. Castle with some detachment because anemia seemed to be more in the scientific precinct of an M.D. than of a chemist.

"Cells have always seemed to me to be too complicated for chemists really to take an interest in what they were doing," he says. "But I really became interested when Dr. Castle said that the red blood cells were twisted out of shape—like a sickle, in fact. He added that they were crescent-shaped in the venous blood, flattened spheres in the arterial blood."

At that point, Professor Pauling wondered why red cells in arterial blood should be any different from red cells in venous blood. Realizing that the answer might be a clue to the mystery of sickle-cell anemia he reached this conclusion: "Venous blood is on its way to the lungs. It has visited the tissue and the oxygen has been taken away from the hemoglobin molecule. But when it gets back to the lungs, the hemoglobin picks up oxygen again and forms *oxyhemoglobin*, which then passes into the arteries."

Dr. Pauling reasoned that the sickle-cell hemoglobin is especially vulnerable when it no longer carries oxygen molecules on its surface. At that point, the abnormal hemoglobin molecules clamp onto one another; the second to the first, the third to the second and so on, forming a long rod of clumped-together hemoglobin molecules in the red blood cell.

"This long rod would then line up with similar rods,"

he theorized. "General forces of attraction would bring them together, forming a long needle-like crystal. As this crystal grows, it becomes larger than the diameter of the cell, continuing to grow until it twists the cell into that abnormal sickle shape."

Back in 1949, while Professor Pauling was beginning his experiments with sickle-cell anemia, it was popularly believed that everybody had the same type of hemoglobin in his red blood cells. But Harvey Itano, then a young graduate student at Caltech, along with Dr. S. J. Singer and Dr. I. C. Wells, soon proved that something was biochemically awry in the blood of sickle-cell anemia patients.

Using a technique called electrophoresis, which can characterize proteins according to the way they move in an electrical field, the Caltech research team discovered that the sickle cell's hemoglobin molecule was a little more positively charged than the normal molecule. They also proved that sickle-cell anemia patients had 100 percent of the abnormally charged molecules in their blood, while subjects with the sickle-cell trait (only one sickle-cell gene) had a mixture of both hemoglobin types, as would be expected.

Professor Pauling was confident that if there was a difference in the electrical charge in the two hemoglobin molecules, it must be due to some slight chemical variation in the hemoglobin molecules themselves. But the problem was easier to state than solve. Hemoglobin is a highly complicated molecule, containing four twisted chains of amino acid building blocks, a total of some 600 amino acids in all. Where in that molecular maze was the chemical clinker that would solve the sickle-cell riddle?

In 1956, seven years after Dr. Pauling's paper on the sickle-cell problem appeared in the journal *Science*, a young chemist named Vernon Ingram came up with the answer. Dr. Ingram was then at the Medical Research Council in Cambridge, England, and now works at MIT in Cambridge, Massachusetts. He pioneered a fascinating analytical technique called peptide fingerprinting, and he put it to work to unravel the mystery of the abnormal hemoglobin molecules. Following this technique, proteins such as hemoglobin are chemically fragmented into smaller portions called peptides. These peptides can then be analyzed to determine what amino acids they contain.

To break down the abnormal and normal hemoglobin molecules, Dr. Ingram treated each with an enzyme called trypsin. This enzyme neatly splits the hemoglobin molecules up and down the length of their protein chains, leaving the chemist with two complex jumbles of peptide fragments. To separate the peptides, he used a combination of electrophoresis and another standard technique called paper chromatography.

After the chromatographic paper was treated with a special dye, the separated peptide fragments showed up in the patterns shown in Fig. 1. Each hemoglobin molecule—normal and sickle cell—broke down into twenty-six different peptide fingerprints—identical in every location except at peptide number four.

Further chemical analysis of the number four peptides told Dr. Ingram that the sickle-cell hemoglobin was indeed different from the normal hemoglobin, but only slightly so. It lacked *one* amino acid building block called *glutamic acid*, and in its place was another amino acid called *valine*. That tiny chemical difference of one amino acid—1/600th of the entire hemoglobin molecule—was

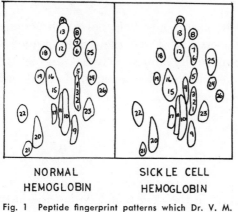

NORMAL
HEMOGLOBIN

SICKLE CELL
HEMOGLOBIN

Fig. 1 Peptide fingerprint patterns which Dr. V. M. Ingram used to pin down the chemical differences between normal hemoglobin and sickle-cell hemoglobin. Fingerprint 4 near the center of each pattern is obviously different but all others are identical. *Biochimica et Biophysica Acta, Vol. 28, permission of Dr. Vernon M. Ingram*

enough to trigger all the pain and misery passed on from generation to generation since the first mutant sickle-cell gene appeared in Africa an unknown number of years ago.

Although researchers now know the biochemical basis of sickle-cell anemia, there is no known cure for this tragic disease. The reason is that biochemists are still not able to repair the genetic disorder that relentlessly forces the body to make molecule after molecule of abnormal hemoglobin, creating its own tragic destiny from some hereditary flaw now lost in the shrouded past of man's evolution. Perhaps this will be possible someday, but scientists cautiously avoid undue optimism on this score.

Sickle-cell anemia is a vivid example of the biochemical chaos that can result when an abnormal gene precipitates and controls the production of an abnormal protein—in this case, hemoglobin. Enzymes are also proteins, and they too rely on a flawless message from the genes if they are to carry out their normal functions as indispensable overseers of the thousands of metabolic processes that make the human body tick. In fact, enzymes are so indispensable that they even guide the construction of the genes themselves.

### INTRODUCING PKU

Because they are proteins, enzymes are also prey to inborn errors in the genes, and within the last few years, biochemists have been uncovering one such hereditary abnormality after another. One of the best known is a disease called phenylketonuria, or PKU for short.

PKU was first observed by the Norwegian physician Asbjörn Fölling in 1934. Its chief symptom is progessive mental retardation, leaving most victims with an average I.Q. of about 50. Other serious effects of the disease are epileptic-like convulsions, eczema, a decrease in normal pigmentation of the skin, eyes and hair, and abnormal brain wave patterns on the chart of an electroencephalogram.

As soon as physicians took note of the disease, which up until then was just another mysterious form of mental retardation, other scientists tried to pinpoint its biochemical origin. Some answers came quickly.

Fölling's clinical tests showed that phenylketonuric patients excreted abnormal amounts of a substance called phenylpyruvic acid in their urine—up to two grams a day in some cases. Other biochemists noted unusually high concentrations of a material called phenylalanine in the bloodstream.

Phenylalanine, an amino acid that makes up about 5 percent of the average nutritionally well-balanced diet, is normally built into the protein of various important body tissues, and the tremendous excess—up to twenty times normal in some patients—serves no useful purpose. In fact, it was suspected of causing the brain damage characteristic of PKU. When all goes well, phenylalanine is converted into another important amino acid called tyrosine, but the phenylpyruvic acid in the urine showed that great quantities of an abnormal metabolite were being formed instead.

Another important finding soon followed in 1957, when Dr. C. A. Jervis discovered that PKU patients lacked an important enzyme called phenylalanine hydroxylase. This is the enzyme that normally converts phenylalanine into tyrosine, and its lack must be tied to some abnormality in the genes of the PKU patient.

To a chemist, the normal and PKU metabolism of phenylalanine would diagrammatically look like Fig. 2.

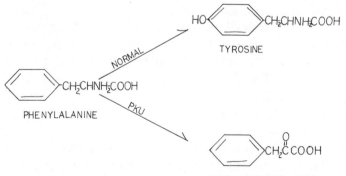

Fig. 2  Normally the amino acid phenylalanine, which forms part of a typical diet, is converted to tyrosine in the body. In PKU, however, the phenylalanine is converted to the abnormal metabolite, phenylpyruvic acid.

Until recently, suspicions were strong, but evidence inconclusive, that phenylalanine caused the mental retardation that accompanied phenylketonuria. However, in 1965, Dr. Harry F. Harlow and Harry Waisman of the University of Wisconsin gave the evidence a boost when they fed infant monkeys a diet high in phenylalanine and brought on several symptoms of the disease in the laboratory animals.

Soon after the discovery of high levels of phenylpyruvic acid in the urine of PKU patients, chemists seized on this fact as a potentially useful method of diagnosis. They knew that a material called ferric chloride turned a bright green color in the presence of phenylpyruvic acid, and that it worked when applied to the diaper of an afflicted child. Enthusiasm for such a test was sparked by the mounting evidence from all over the world that a very restricted, low phenylalanine diet could spare young children a bleak future of progressive mental retardation if the disease was detected in infancy.

The ferric chloride test was soon used in many hospitals throughout the country, but it had a few admitted shortcomings. Occasionally it showed up a false positive, but an even more serious objection was that it was not really effective until the child was about six weeks old. By that time, the child was out of the hospital, away from a doctor's care, and serious brain damage could have already occurred without the parents even being aware of it.

To get around the shortcomings of the ferric chloride test, researchers set out to develop an unequivocal test that could determine high phenylalanine concentrations in small amounts of the newborn infant's blood. Not only would such a test be useful for diagnosing the disease, but it could also be used to monitor the phenylalanine levels

of a child living on the increasingly popular low-phenyl-
alanine diet.

Of all the blood tests developed, one of the most
effective is the brainchild of Dr. Robert Guthrie of the
Buffalo Medical School Children's Hospital. The Guthrie
test requires only a few drops of blood from the infant's
toe or heel, and it can pick up abnormal phenylalanine
levels when the child is as young as four days old.

Called a "bacterial inhibition assay," Dr. Guthrie's
ingenious test depends on the growth of bacteria with
the euphonious name of *Bacillus subtilis.* Normally, a
chemical substance called beta-2-thienylalanine will inhibit the growth of these bacteria on an agar plate. However, even low concentrations of phenylalanine in the
blood will override the effects of the inhibitor, and allow
*Bacillus subtilis* to grow normally. The rate of growth is a
measure of the amount of phenylalanine—a level of more
than 4 milligrams/100 cubic centimeters being considered
suspicious and requiring further diagnosis. A typical
scheme for carrying out the Guthrie test is shown in
Figs. 3-a,b,c.

Between early 1962 and the end of 1963, more than
400,000 newborn infants in hospitals in twenty-nine states
were given the Guthrie test. That it proved its worth was
evident from the thirty-nine confirmed cases of PKU uncovered, almost double the disease incidence of the previously expected figure of one in 20,000. Many of the
children found to have PKU are now living a relatively
normal life on the low phenylalanine diet which is discussed at more length below.

Hospitals in all fifty states are now using the Guthrie
test or some modification of it to detect PKU, a project
strongly supported by the Children's Bureau of the United

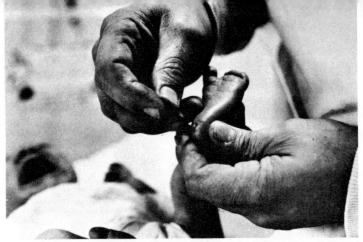

Fig. 3a In the first step of the Guthrie blood test for PKU, a drop of blood is removed from the infant's heel.

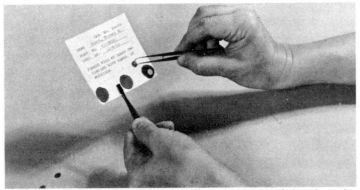

Fig. 3b The blood sample is absorbed on filter paper and mailed to the testing laboratory. *Robert Guthrie*

Fig. 3c The wide halo indicated by the arrow on the agar plate shows that there is phenylalanine in the blood sample and a possibility of PKU. Further diagnosis must then be made. The other circles on the plate show that there is not enough phenylalanine in those blood samples to encourage the growth of the bacteria that produce the halo effect. The upper row contains the "control" blood samples of known phenylalanine content.

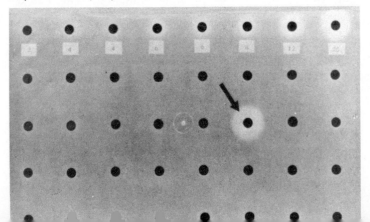

States Department of Health, Education, and Welfare. The number of testing hospitals varies from state to state, but more than half have passed laws to make the test mandatory, except where it conflicts with the religious beliefs of the parents involved.

Even before the link between PKU and high blood levels of phenylalanine became as strong as it is now, physicians were convinced that a very restricted diet might effectively halt the course of the disease in afflicted children—particularly if it was detected at an early age.

Specifications for the diet would be uncompromisingly strict: nutritionally well balanced but low in phenylalanine. It would not be an easy menu to create because most food staples, including milk, meat, eggs, cheese and bread, contain high concentrations of phenylalanine. Another consideration was that the diet would have to contain at least some phenylalanine if children were to build up tissue that they just could not do without.

In spite of the obstacles, in 1954 Dr. Horst Bickel of the Universitäts-Kinderklinik in Marburg, Germany, was able to devise and try a low phenylalanine diet for a two-year-old PKU patient. Results were excellent: further mental deterioration and other serious symptoms were averted. Since then, nutritionists and dieticians have been developing refinements of that original diet with the same outstanding results and a minimum of grumbling from the children who have to endure it.

Dr. Richard Koch, Director of the Child Development Clinic at Children's Hospital in Los Angeles, added to the previously encouraging results of the PKU diet, when he recently reported the following case histories:

"The most spectacular gains occurred in a case who was diagnosed at eight months with a developmental quotient of 37. At five years of age, his I.Q. was 79. Another youngster, age three years and two months, was put on dietary therapy at the insistence of his mother. His initial I.Q. was 10. Much to our amazement he has made steady progress and his most recent I.Q. at seven years of age was 53. At present, he is in a class for educable mentally retarded children, has developed language ability and behaves nicely."

One of the chief staples of the restricted diet is a milk substitute called Lofenalac®, a casein hydrolysate containing fat, carbohydrates and some vitamins. A bright side of the diet is that a high carbohydrate intake is essential to meet calorie requirements, which means that gumdrops, jelly beans, Popsicles and lollipops are completely acceptable.

In a typical breakfast diet recommended by several pediatric hospitals, a four-year-old PKU patient could eat a double serving of puffed wheat, several orange slices and eight ounces of Lofenalac. For dinner the same child might have two tablespoonfuls of mashed yams, four tablespoonfuls of sliced bananas, two tablespoonfuls of cooked cauliflower, four tablespoonfuls of shredded raw cabbage with 2 teaspoonfuls of mayonnaise and another eight-ounce glass of Lofenalac.

Almost every child needs his own special dietary mixture, which varies with the amount of phenylalanine his blood contains at any one time. Once the blood level is lowered to normal the diet can be considerably less restricted and made a little more attractive to the child.

Because the PKU diet has seen widespread use only since the late fifties, scientists still do not know if it must be maintained for a lifetime. Nutrition experts at the Delaware State Board of Health have evidence that it may be possible to discontinue the diet shortly after a child reaches the age of four. But they add the strong qualification that the diet must have been started when the child was *four months old or younger*. Spotted throughout the world are other case histories that seem to support the Delaware findings.

### HISTIDINEMIA

Encouraged by the dramatic success of biochemists and nutritionists in giving new hope to PKU patients, pediatricians all over the world carefully tested any children who gave even slight evidences of the disease. Among these pediatricians were Dr. H. Ghadimi and Dr. M. W. Partington of Toronto, who ran the standard PKU diagnostic tests on a child whose speech development seemed to be progressing more slowly than usual.

When the Canadian physicians ran the ferric chloride urine test for PKU, the results were positive. The familiar green color appeared, apparently indicating the presence of the abnormal metabolite—phenylpyruvic acid. But they were more than a little surprised when the blood test for abnormal levels of phenylalanine was *negative*.

Perplexed by the contradiction in the two tests, the two pediatricians called on the talents of the veteran Canadian biochemist Andrew Hunter. His careful analysis of the blood, urine and cerebrospinal fluid of the afflicted child showed that phenylalanine levels were normal, but that they all contained high levels of another important amino acid, histidine. Accordingly, pediatricians were alerted to be on the lookout for other cases.

Close on the heels of the Canadian findings, a four-year-old child showed up at St. Christopher's Hospital for Children in Philadelphia, where Dr. Victor Auerbach and Dr. Angelo M. DiGeorge were confronted with the same strangely conflicting results: *positive* urine test for PKU, *negative* blood test for phenylalanine, and *positive* blood test for the newly discovered disease called histidinemia.

But the question still remained: What turned the ferric chloride test paper green? Dr. Auerbach believed that the confused result was probably due to some other metabolite connected with histidinemia, just as phenylpyruvic acid was linked with PKU.

He soon found that a material called imidazolepyruvic acid was the culprit, and was doubly pleased to note that this compound was a so-called keto acid, the same type of chemical compound produced in PKU.

Probing even deeper into the erratic biochemistry of the disease, Dr. Auerbach and his colleague, Dr. Robert Baldridge of Temple University Medical School, proved that histidinemia patients could not convert histidine to a material called urocanic acid, as normal people could. Instead the biochemical machinery produced large amounts of imidazolepyruvic acid as the color test showed. They immediately suspected that the enzyme needed for normal metabolism was missing, indicating strongly that this was another inborn error of metabolism, such as PKU.

Their suspicions proved correct when in 1962 Dr. Bert La Du at NYU's School of Medicine showed that normal individuals contained an enzyme, called histidase, in their skins that histidinemic children lacked. And since histidase, like all other enzymes, is a protein, its absence must certainly be attributed to a genetic flaw similar to that encountered in PKU.

In more recent developments, Dr. Baldridge and his Temple colleagues were able to duplicate the biochemical aspects of the disease in laboratory rats by feeding them diets high in histidine. Even though it was obviously impossible to mimic retarded speech development in the animals, the diet did cause them to produce the abnormal metabolite—imidazolepyruvic acid.

It should be noted here that histidinemia is a very new disease and its symptoms have still not been completely pinpointed. So far they seem to range from mild speech difficulties to severe mental retardation. Scientists are experimenting with a low histidine diet, even though the approach is nowhere near as clear-cut as it was with the low phenylalanine diet and PKU. One complication is the fact that older children and adults produce histidine in their bodies, *without* taking that amino acid in with their food. Therefore, a low histidine diet alone is not considered to be the complete answer at this time.

### WILSON'S DISEASE

Aside from the fact that they are all "inborn errors of metabolism," sickle-cell anemia, PKU and histidinemia have something else in common. Their biochemical and physiological symptoms usually show up when a child is still very young, becoming worse almost every day as the victim tries to cope with an environment in which he is a kind of "genetic cripple."

Wilson's disease is a little different. This hereditary disorder can also be spotted in infancy, but its more serious effects do not usually show up until the patient is much older, forty or fifty in some cases. The disease—first described by Dr. S. A. K. Wilson—damages the brain and liver as the result of the accumulation of large amounts of copper in those organs. Like sickle-cell anemia, PKU and histidinemia, the disease ultimately results from the fact that a child has inherited one abnormal gene from each of his parents.

Wilson's disease is very rare, with probably not more than a thousand cases in the United States and perhaps twenty times that many in the entire world, according to an estimate of Dr. I. Herbert Scheinberg, professor of Medicine at Albert Einstein Medical College in New York. The disease is associated with hereditary lack of the protein ceruloplasmin, which binds copper atoms.

In 1959, Dr. Philip Aisen, a physician, and Professor Anatol Morell, a chemist, both working with Dr. Scheinberg, helped perfect a simple diagnostic test that is particularly useful for spotting the ceruloplasmin deficiency in infants. In the test, a drop of blood taken from the child's heel or toe is placed on a piece of filter paper impregnated with a substance called paraphenylene diamine. The paper is then warmed to 40 degrees centigrade for five minutes. If a light brown circle appears, ceruloplasmin is absent or diminished in amount; if a blue circle appears, darker than a control, a normal amount of ceruloplasmin is present. Ceruloplasmin levels can now also be measured exactly by automated techniques using one drop of blood.

Within the past few years, Dr. Aisen has tested blood serum samples of hundreds of infants and adults for the ceruloplasmin deficiency, and some of these individuals are now being treated for Wilson's disease at Albert Einstein College of Medicine and elsewhere. At the present, the best treatment is a combination of drugs and diet, both aimed at reducing or preventing abnormal copper accumulations in the body.

Drugs useful against Wilson's disease are known to chemists as chelating agents because of their peculiar molecular structure. Chelating agents have tiny "molecular claws" that can surround a copper atom and remove it from the body before it can damage the liver, brain or other sensitive tissue. As an etymological footnote, the word "chelate" comes from the Greek word *chela* which means claw. One of the drugs—called BAL—was first administered by Dr. John Cumings of England, and was originally designed as a war gas antidote. Another even more useful drug—called penicillamine—is a chemical relative of the well-known antibiotic penicillin, and was first used by Dr. John Walshe of Cambridge, England.

As for the diet, a Wilson's disease patient must keep away from mushrooms, oysters, nuts, chocolates, liver and other foods rich in copper. According to Dr. Scheinberg, the combined therapy of drugs and diet may not only avert the onset of the disease, but it can dramatically improve the condition of patients in the advanced stages of Wilson's disease. He illustrates with these case histories:

"About nine years ago, a little twelve-year-old girl was brought to us, so ill that she could not walk. We diagnosed her condition as Wilson's disease, and began treatment immediately. We have treated her for the last nine years, and she has made a remarkable recovery in that period. She is married now, working and leading a relatively normal life.

"We also tested her younger brother when she was brought to us. He was only ten months old at the time, and seemed perfectly healthy. But his blood serum showed a complete absence of ceruloplasmin. As a preventive measure we began treatment, and nine years later, the boy still seems perfectly healthy. However, we will not really be certain we have delayed onset of the disease until he becomes a little older; perhaps fifteen to twenty years old.

"As far as actual treatment goes, we have had several advanced Wilson's disease patients who have been bedridden and totally incapacitated; indeed in some instances given up as hopeless. Using the combination drug-diet treatment, we have been able to restore these people to a virtually normal existence by removal of copper from their system."


## TAY-SACHS DISEASE

Because they are the result of a single genetic mutation, inborn errors of metabolism originate in one place at one time—but they do not usually stay there. As the original gene carrier or his children move to another town, another province, another nation, the edges of the gene pool extend a little farther with each move. A case in point is sickle-cell anemia; once found only in Africa, it is now widespread throughout the United States. Similarly, the hemoglobin disorder thalassemia has permitted anthropologists to trace the migrations of people from Sicily—where the gene seems to have originated—to many other parts of the world. One such "cultural" disease is Tay-Sachs disease.

Tay-Sachs disease is found largely in Jews who live or have lived in northeastern Europe. Unlike Wilson's disease, which does not become really serious until relatively late in life, Tay-Sachs disease hits hard in infancy. First observed by two physicians, Drs. Warren Tay and Bernard P. Sachs, the disease takes its lethal toll early in life, usually before the child reaches the age of three. The symptoms are apparent from shortly after birth: the child becomes abnormally irritable with little provocation, reacts excessively to sudden noises, and fails to grow and develop normally. An ophthalmologist can recognize the disease by a typical red "cherry spot" in the retina of the eye.

Just a few years ago, almost nothing was known about the biochemical aspects of Tay-Sachs disease, except that it was obviously a severe neurological disorder. More recently researchers at Albert Einstein Medical College and elsewhere have combined the special talents of the pathologist, chemist and electron microscopist to develop a finely detailed composite picture of the damage that the disease causes in brain cells.

It is known that Tay-Sachs disease is a so-called lipidosis of the brain cells, an accumulation of fatty substances that swell the cells to triple their normal size. The lipids take over space that normally belongs to other cell constituents to such an extent that the cell cannot operate properly and dies. Researchers have been looking at the swollen brain cells—or neurons—under an ordinary microscope for several years, but Albert Einstein's Dr. Robert Terry thought that a closer look through the powerful eye of the electron microscope might reveal some more definite clues as to what had gone wrong in the damaged brain cells.

At low magnification, Dr. Terry's microscope picked out grainy areas in the neurons of Tay-Sachs patients that were not found in normal tissue. But that was not the answer he was looking for, so he prepared for an even closer look by slicing the affected brain tissue into cuts less than a millionth of an inch thick. Then as he increased the magnification from 4,000 to 100,000 times normal, the granular shapes appeared as a series of laminated layers. A blown-up photograph of the abnormal areas showed that these Tay-Sachs "organelles" were really a series of concentric circles or whorls, dark areas alternating with white.

Once they knew what they were looking for, the late Dr. Saul Korey and his group in the Albert Einstein Department of Neurology set out to discover what they could about the chemical makeup of the organelles, or "membranous cytoplasmic bodies," as Dr. Terry dubbed them. Supplied with a three-gram sample of diseased brain tissue by Dr. Bruno Volk of Jewish Chronic Disease Hospital, they used a technique called differential centrifuga-

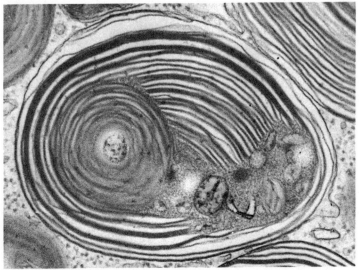

Fig. 4a   Electron photomicrograph shows how the membranous cytoplasmic bodies distribute themselves in the brain cells of patients afflicted with Tay-Sachs disease. *Journal of Neuropathology and Experimental Pathology, Vol. 22*

Fig. 4b   A close-up look at the affected cell in Fig. 4a magnified 120,000 times normal by Dr. Robert Terry. *Journal of Neuropathology and Experimental Pathology, Vol. 22*

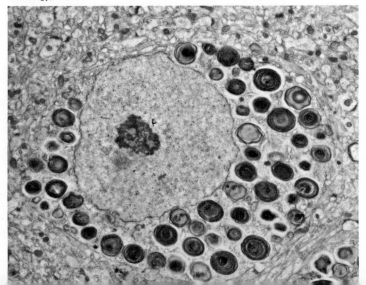

tion to separate the organelles from the rest of the tissue.

Chemical analysis of the organelles by Dr. Stanley Samuels revealed that the bulk of the organelles was made up of sugar-containing substances called gangliosides. They also consisted of protein, fatty substances called phospholipids, large amounts of cholesterol and other sugar-containing substances called cerebrosides.

No one knows why the organelles take the shape they do in the brain, but the Albert Einstein researchers suspected that the shape must be related to physical and chemical affinities among the four components. When they mixed the four together in a test tube in the proper proportions and looked at the result under an electron microscope, they became more certain. The organelle ingredients apparently re-formed themselves into the same series of spiraling concentric circles found in the brain tissue of Tay-Sachs patients.

The Tay-Sachs disease problem is still far from solved. The solution is complicated by the fact that all four components of the organelles are found *both* in normal and diseased brain tissue. Dr. Korey proposed that at least part of the answer may lie in the abnormal amounts of gangliosides found in the Tay-Sachs cells. He suggested that the abnormal cell may lack an enzyme that normally breaks down the gangliosides in normal tissue before they can accumulate and damage the brain cell, and further observations seem to bear this out.

## OTHER INBORN ERRORS

As scientists become more familiar with the biochemical earmarks of inborn errors of metabolism, they are compiling a long list of these inherited diseases—some that can be treated, some that cannot.

Many of these diseases, such as albinism, alkaptonuria, pentosuria and galactosemia, are marked by the lack of an important enzyme, the function of which is to convert some common component of the diet into a useful and/or harmless metabolite.

In galactosemia, for instance, patients lack an enzyme that converts the common milk sugar galactose into a useful metabolite. The result, as in PKU, is mental retardation, which can be circumvented through the use of a galactose-free diet.

Diabetes mellitus—or sugar diabetes—is one of the best-known inborn errors of metabolism, resulting in part at least from a deficiency of insulin—a hormonal protein whose complete chemical structure and total synthesis were recently determined. The success of insulin administration in treating diabetes needs no elaboration in this discussion.

Goitrous cretinism is also in the "autosomal recessive" category of hereditary diseases, and its symptoms, including mental retardation, evolve from a lack of the hormone thyroxin. Again the course of this disease can be restrained by intelligent administration of the missing hormone.

Although most inborn errors of metabolism make themselves known when they encounter naturally occurring substances that they are not equipped to handle, others leap into prominence when they encounter chemical substances man deliberately adds to his own biochemical environment. Drugs are one instance of this.

Some scientists suggest that modern medicine is really creating forces that work against themselves: some drugs which are given to cure a certain ailment may encounter carriers of certain genes that are adversely affected by that drug.

For instance, the anesthetic succinyl choline should not be used by certain people because it may cause prolonged anesthesia. It is now known that some patients lack an enzyme that would ordinarily remove the drug from the bloodstream in a very short time.

Isoniazid, a drug used to treat tuberculosis, must be administered with great caution because about half the people in the United States may be genetically unequipped to handle it. With the proper enzyme, some people metabolize isoniazid quickly enough so that it does its intended job without adverse side reactions. Without the enzyme, a wide variety of abnormal reactions may take place. The genetic basis of these abnormal reactions is evident from the fact that the ratio of "slow metabolizers" to "fast metabolizers" varies from country to country and race to race. In Latin America slow metabolizers make up about a third of the population; among Eskimos only 5 percent cannot tolerate the drug.

Other individuals, because they lack an enzyme called glucose-6-phosphate dehydrogenase, are abnormally sensitive to primaquine, a widely used antimalarial drug. The incidence of this gene-based abnormality varies from almost zero in Ashkenazic Jews to high in Greeks. In addition, the sensitivity seems to be linked to the chromosomes that determine the sex of an individual; women are much less sensitive than are men.

Since these drug abnormalities first appeared, the new field of pharmacogenetics has developed, which is aimed at spotting the gene-caused sensitivities before a drug has been given. For example, NYU's Dr. Bert La Du, who is one of the most active and earliest entries in the new field, has developed a simple test that can quickly determine whether or not a patient should be anesthetized with succinyl choline.

Dr. La Du believes that with a more complete understanding of the chemical and genetic bases of adverse drug reactions, more good drugs will reach a greater number of people. At the present time, a drug can be kept off or removed from the market because of an ill effect observed in only a small number of people. If the ill effect is caused by a genetic deficiency, it could mean that many people without that deficiency are prevented from using a drug that could save them from death. Human society does best—in a health sense—when its genetic background hews to a well-adjusted norm. Taken in this sense, "good" genes advance the well-being of the race; "bad" genes struggle against its continuing progress. On the surface, genes triggering sickle-cell anemia, PKU and Wilson's disease are genes we are better off without, and in most cases the surface appraisal continues to have genuine substance.

The sickle-cell gene is undoubtedly a "bad" gene when it becomes affiliated with another sickle-cell gene. The fate of a child with the two-sickle-cell-gene condition was detailed earlier. On the other hand, carriers of the single-sickle-cell gene are resistant to malaria. Since the gene originated in Africa, it would seem to have an obvious advantage on that continent where malaria is still widespread. To geneticists, this is a so-called "balanced polymorphism"—the disadvantage being balanced by the advantage—which is all well and good in a malaria environment. But what about elsewhere?

Dr. Anthony Allison of England completed a comprehensive genetic survey showing that the sickle-cell gene is *declining* among American Negroes; the African incidence of 30 percent as contrasted with 10 percent in the United States. The gene is dying out because sickle-cell anemia patients—bearers of the double dose—are dying

out. But the carriers of the single gene continue to propa-
gate in America's malaria-free environment with the gene
certainly no advantage at all.

There is a test for the single-sickle-cell gene, and many
scientists, including Linus Pauling, believe that potential
carriers and their spouses or prospective spouses should
take the test before considering having children. Professor
Pauling puts it this way:

"Two people who carry the gene would have to think
carefully about their responsibilities with respect to bring-
ing children into the world, where according to Men-
delian laws of heredity, there is the 25 percent chance
for each child to have the disease.

"For the child, this means a series of crises occurring
over and over again: severe chills, recurrent infections.
Because he does not have as good protection against infection as other people, he finally dies, usually in his
childhood or early teens.

"But if the children were not born at all, that would
be a better way of getting rid of the gene, not at the cost
of human suffering, but through the use of human intelligence."

Even though there is no known cure for sickle-cell
anemia, earlier sections of this chapter illustrate that
something can be done for other inborn errors. In the
case of PKU, galactosemia and Wilson's disease, a restricted diet plus other therapy can make the difference
between a tragically deprived life and a relatively normal one. Yet the gene disorder itself has not been cured,
and when these afflicted individuals marry, they certainly
will pass the flaw on to their children, as Dr. Pauling
pointed out. Viewed from that vantage point, medical
progress is contributing to a larger pool of abnormal
genes. Is this good or bad?

Many researchers are not sure, but the optimists are confident that it is within the potential of science to rectify the gene disorder at its source, even though this may not be possible for decades. Others, including Dr. Bert La Du, believe that these abnormal genes are part of man's evolution, and in that respect, are not an evil.

"It is the variation in genes that allows man and other species to change gradually as environment changes," says Dr. La Du. "What we are seeing are the signs of nature experimenting to develop the most suitable background to cope with our environment. While some of these may lead to clinical signs and symptoms that we may have to deal with as medical problems, the overall variation is a part of life. If we did not have this ability to explore new genes and variations of genes, it is unlikely that man would have the future ability to cope with environmental changes."

# CHAPTER 3

## DARWIN'S WARM LITTLE POND

Is it possible that if every living thing, plant and animal, were suddenly to disappear from the face of the earth, life as we know it would probably never again evolve?

That is one of the many questions now facing a new breed of scientists—probably not more than three dozen in all—who are trying to duplicate chemical events that may have occurred four and a half billion years ago. These scientists believe that the long process of evolution from the simplest organic chemical to the first living thing must have had its ultimate root in an accumulation of physical forces and chemical reactions that existed near the beginning of the Earth's geological history, and perhaps only then.

As background for their laboratory simulation of early Earth, the "chemical evolutionists" adopted several working tenets which seem to be geologically acceptable and chemically sound. Their starting point is a surprisingly simple mixture—the four constituents of an atmosphere that no longer surrounds our planet, an atmosphere that would quickly destroy contemporary life. They do not deny the importance of the lithosphere (the solid part of the earth) or the hydrosphere (the watery areas), but within the confines of this chapter, the atmospheric constituents will be of primary importance.

According to a working hypothesis now embraced by some chemical evolutionists, the original atmosphere was a "reducing atmosphere," which means that its chief elements (carbon, oxygen and nitrogen) were combined with the element hydrogen, producing an acrid environment of methane, ammonia, water and small amounts of hydrogen itself.

In our contemporary "oxidizing" atmosphere, hydrogen is only a minor element, but oxygen is so abundant that most elements and compounds tend to combine with it or be "oxidized" by it. More and more scientists conjecture that the changeover from one atmosphere to the other mirrored events in which organic compounds switched from a lifeless combination of carbon and other elements to systems that have the most essential earmarks of life— the ability to grow and reproduce.

The earliest record of what may have been living things was found in a piece of South African rock by Harvard's Professor Elso S. Barghoorn in 1965. The stone, believed to be at least three billion years old, contained residues of bacteria-like organisms, so small that 50,000 of them would add up to about an inch in length. A decade earlier, Professor Barghoorn discovered what appeared to be traces of tiny algae in a chunk of Michigan flintstone known to be two billion years old.

Although they are very simple organisms, both algae and bacteria are kept alive by the same biochemical principles that power higher organisms: plants, animals and

| ANCIENT REDUCING ATMOSPHERE * | | | TODAY'S OXIDIZING ATMOSPHERE * | | |
|---|---|---|---|---|---|
| C (carbon) | exists as | $CH_4$ (methane) | C | exists as | $CO_2$ (carbon dioxide) |
| O (oxygen) | exists as | $H_2O$ (water) | O | exists as | $O_2$ (oxygen gas) |
| N (nitrogen) | exists as | $NH_3$ (ammonia) | N | exists as | $N_2$ (nitrogen gas) |
| H (hydrogen) | exists as | $H_2$ (hydrogen gas and in the above combinations) | H | exists as | $H_2O$ (water) |

* These are of course only the principal atmospheric components; others that were less necessary to chemical evolution are not listed here.

man. But between the era that produced the first organic precursors of life and the structures found in Dr. Barghoorn's rock samples there is a yawning chasm of chemical evolution that scientists have only recently begun to explore.

The work of the chemical evolutionist is especially challenging from the point of view that all remnants of the life ingredients that they are attempting to re-create have long disappeared from the earth, and perhaps were devoured by the life forms that followed them. Yet many of these same scientists agree with the Russian biochemist A. I. Oparin that it is possible to understand life only by studying its origin and development.

Any discussion of evolution and the origin of life must necessarily bring in the name of the foremost innovator in the field—Charles Darwin. Although Darwin's brilliant excursions into the origins of the human race begin where the chemical evolutionists leave off, his letter of 1871 on the events that may have preceded the emergence of the first living thing still stands the test of contemporary thought.

". . . But if (and oh what a big if!) we could conceive in some warm little pond, with all sorts of ammonia and phosphoric salts, light, heat, electricity, etc., present, that a proteine compound was chemically formed, ready to undergo still more complex changes . . ." wrote Darwin, and although his words are now nearly a century old, it will be useful to keep them in mind.

### THE ESSENTIAL INGREDIENTS

Any chemist, whether he is studying reactions between two different salts or the chemical ingredients of a new plastic, can usually tell you, by means of a simple chemical equation, what he is doing. On the left side of the equation are the compounds that he puts into the reaction; on the right side are the compounds that he expects to produce. To illustrate *his* aims, the extremely simplified equation drawn by the chemical evolutionist might look something like this:

Water+Ammonia+Methane
  +Hydrogen————————————⟶ Amino acids+proteins
                                      +carbohydrates+fats
                                      +nucleic acids+most
                                      of the other chemical
                                      constituents of every-
                                      thing that lives or has
                                      ever lived.

If he were to underline the two products whose absence would make the equation for life meaningless, our chemical evolutionist would undoubtedly choose *proteins* and *nucleic acids*.

The nucleic acids, forming as they do the basis of the "genetic code," pass hereditary characteristics from generation to generation. They also carry instructions for the manufacture of the thousands of different proteins that go into living tissue, organs and body fluids. The proteins in turn "catalyze" the manufacture of new nucleic acids which tell the cell to make new structural protein, in a fortuitous chemical interplay which in effect keeps the life process in motion. In addition, the cell's production of all the other important components, e.g., the fats, the carbohydrates and the vitamins, depends on the enzymatic activity of the proteins.

## THE ENERGY

Any mixture of chemicals, in a modern laboratory or in the chemical cauldron of the ancient world, remains uncombined unless some form of energy is available to trigger the combination. As for the world of four and a half billion years ago, the chemical evolutionists believe that there was probably more than enough energy available to convert the small molecules of the early atmosphere into the gigantic protein and nucleic acid molecules now found in all living organisms. And fortunately, all these primitive forces can be re-created in the laboratory.

One of the chief energy sources in the primitive world must have been the intense ultraviolet radiation of the sun, according to most researchers in the field, who observe that four and a half billion years ago, the earth was undoubtedly showered with much greater quantities of ultraviolet light than it is today. They theorize that while the ancient reducing atmosphere was relatively transparent to the sun's ultraviolet output, our contemporary atmosphere filters out the bulk of the sun's UV production.

Many geologists assume that the primitive earth was drenched by month-long rainstorms, its atmosphere rent by violent lightning storms. Those early flashes of lightning, generating intensely hot centers of electrical energy, might very well have sparked enough molecular activity to break the atmospheric gases into smaller chemical fragments which then recombined to form the larger chemical ingredients of life.

As the rain fell, large bodies of water formed, which leached salts, including salts of radioactive elements, from the solid Earth's surface. Presumably the ionizing radiation from these salts could also spur the production of organic substances.

Finally, other scientists suggest that heat alone, produced by radiation or volcanic activity, might also have been a major contributor to the energy required for organic synthesis on the primitive earth.

### THE AMINO ACIDS

In 1953, a bolt of artificial lightning flashed in a laboratory at the University of Chicago, sparking the first real hope that important organic molecules could be built up from the primitive reducing atmosphere. Dr. Stanley Miller, then working under the direction of Nobel Laureate Harold C. Urey, sent 60,000 volts of electricity into a series of condensers, flasks and glass tubing containing nothing but ammonia, methane, hydrogen and water vapor. Dr. Urey, incidentally, was among the first to suggest a reducing atmosphere as the starting point for the chemical evolution of organic substances.

For an entire week, Dr. Miller exposed his glass-enclosed replica of the world's primitive atmosphere to artificial lightning. As the experiment progressed, the water vapor condensed and dripped into a "boiling flask" where it was again heated up to a vapor so it could mingle again with the three other gases. Gradually the water in the boiling flask became darker, until, by the time Dr. Miller decided to terminate the experiment, the clear water had turned dark red.

On careful chemical analysis, Miller (now at the University of California in La Jolla) was elated to find that the waters of his man-made primordial ocean contained many organic substances, including the amino acids alanine and glycine. This was important because amino acids are the building blocks for the larger protein molecules that are so necessary to the life process. He also found urea, hydrogen cyanide, formic acid, glycolic acid, and lactic acid, many of which are important elements in the chemical scheme of life. In the opinion of some interested researchers, Dr. Miller's experiment remains "the classic experiment," and "a landmark in the study of chemical evolution."

It should be noted that in 1951, Dr. Melvin Calvin, Nobel Laureate in Chemistry from the University of California, was able to produce organic compounds by irradiating a mixture of carbon dioxide, hydrogen and water. Since then, Dr. Calvin has said that the "reducing" atmosphere used by Dr. Miller was probably more realistic in a geological sense than the one he worked with.

Since Dr. Miller's 1953 experiment, he and other researchers have repeated it, producing many other amino acids and organic substances from the simulated primitive atmosphere. Variations of the Miller work, utilizing other forms of energy—ultraviolet light, bombardment with electrons and gamma rays, and even heat—also produced amino acids from the same mixture of reducing gases. For instance, Juan Oro at the University of Houston showed that amino acids could be produced simply by passing water, ammonia and water vapor through a tube heated to about 1,300 degrees Fahrenheit.

Of all the energy sources hypothetically available for the formation of organic substances from the primitive atmosphere, heat from volcanoes or hot streams has been considered highly inadequate by some observers. However, Dr. Sidney Fox and his colleagues at the Institute for Molecular Evolution of the University of Miami are convinced that such thermal areas were adequate energy sources in ancient times. Dr. Fox and his co-worker Kaoru Harada passed the atmospheric elements through a variety of solid materials, including silica sand, volcanic lava and alumina, each of which is found in abundance on the surface of the Earth. The solids were heated to temperatures ranging from 950 to 1,050 degrees centigrade, temperatures known to exist in the mouths of contemporary active volcanoes, Dr. Fox points out. According to the Fox theory, elements of the ancient atmosphere undoubtedly came into contact with hot spots on the Earth's surface, and when they did, many different organic substances were formed. These were then probably washed into the sea or other bodies of water.

The Florida researchers think their experiments are especially pertinent to the origin of life, because they produced fourteen of the eighteen amino acids most commonly found in natural protein, and no amino acids not found in nature. For the record, the amino acids produced in the "hot sands" of Dr. Fox's laboratory were aspartic acid, threonine, serine, glutamic acid, proline, glycine, alanine, valine, arginine, isoleucine, allisoleucine, leucine, tyrosine, phenylalanine, lysine and alpha-aminobutyric acid.

When Dr. Fox first reported that he had been able to make amino acids using sand, heat and the components of the reducing atmosphere, some scientists argued that his results were chemically interesting, but geologically unrealistic. Volcanoes occur so infrequently on the Earth's surface, said the critics, that their role in the manufacture of organic substances in early times must have been very minor. However, the geologist F. M. Bullard points out that there are still about 400 active volcanoes on the Earth, and that these are probably only a small fraction of their number on the early Earth. Volcanic activity was so widespread in the Earth's formative years, says Dr. Bullard, that large areas of the American Northwest—more than 200,000 square miles, in fact—are covered by basaltic lava that is a half mile deep in some places. Similar areas exist elsewhere in the world.

Even before he reported his findings on the role of thermal energy in the creation of amino acids from the hypothetical atmosphere of the past, Dr. Fox had shown that heat was probably a very important factor in forming giant protein molecules from their smaller building blocks. In this case, the heat came from the much milder temperatures in thermal zones that occur near geysers and hot springs, for example.

In 1958, the Fox group was able to show that if they heated a mixture of amino acids together at temperatures of about 170 degrees centigrade, the amino acids would link themselves together in long chainlike molecules that were very much like proteins in many of their physical and chemical properties. Dr. Fox dubbed these interesting long molecules "proteinoids."

Again, the Florida researchers' results sent a ripple through the ranks of other organic chemists who knew that if they heated amino acids to more than the boiling point of water (100 degrees centigrade), the whole experiment went up in smoke or solidified into a tarry mass from which it was impossible to isolate anything. As it turned out, Dr. Fox had introduced a synthetic wrinkle that hadn't been tried in the past. He learned that if he used the proper proportions of two key amino acids—aspartic acid and glutamic acid—then mixed them with any or all of the other "naturally occurring" amino acids, they combined easily into long "proteinoid" chains without degenerating into smoke or an insoluble tar.

Since 1960, Drs. Fox and Harada, along with researchers in other parts of the world, found that proteinoids can be prepared at temperatures of less than 100 degrees centigrade if they are mixed with phosphorus-containing catalysts that may have existed in the rocks and oceans of the primitive earth.

In still later work, Dr. Fox suggests that the proteinoids might also have been the structural ancestors of the first living cell. But at this point, it might be useful to pursue the efforts of the chemical evolutionists who want to know how other essential life ingredients may have formed on the right-hand side of that equation for life.

## THE NUCLEIC ACIDS

Chemically, nucleic acids are larger molecules and almost as complex as proteins. Proteins are essentially long chains of amino acids linked together in more or less complicated arrangements. Their molecular weights (their relative weights in comparison to an atom of hydrogen) range from about 6,000 to about 66,000. Nucleic acids, on the other hand, are composed of smaller nucleotide units, which form themselves into chains with molecular weights in the millions. But it is more complicated than that. Each nucleotide unit is really three molecules in one—being a combination of a base, a sugar and

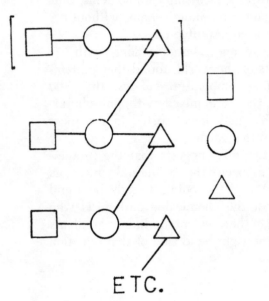

BASE

SUGAR

PHOSPHATE

ETC.

Fig. 5 Within the bracket is a single nucleotide, which may be attached to thousands of other nucleotides to make the nucleic acid chains that contain the hereditary memory of every living cell.

In RNA, or ribosenucleic acid, the sugar is always ribose, but the base may be either adenine, guanine, cytosine or *uracil*.

In DNA, or deoxyribosenucleic acid, the sugar is always deoxyribose, but the base may be either adenine, guanine, cytosine or *thymine*.

The DNA is a chemical template which feeds the RNA molecule its instructions for making protein molecules from smaller amino acid building blocks. It has been shown that a grouping of three nucleotides is usually responsible for building a single amino acid into the overall protein molecule. For example, three uridine nucleotides are responsible for placing the amino acid alanine into a larger protein molecule. If the uridine were replaced by another nucleotide, the new triplet would produce a different amino acid.

a phosphate. The two most important nucleic acids are known as deoxyribosenucleic acid (DNA) and ribosenucleic acid (RNA). DNA usually controls the production of RNA, which in turn is overseer for assembling proteins from their amino acid building blocks. Chemically they are very similar except for the fact that the DNA unit lacks an oxygen atom found in all RNA units.

At first glance, the problem of synthesizing nucleic acids under supposed primitive Earth conditions looks a little overwhelming. Not only does the chemist have to account for the formation of the individual nucleotide units of the nucleic acid chains, but he must also explain the formation of the three different nucleotide components—the base, the sugar and the phosphate. In effect, it is a "boxes within boxes" situation.

As an example of the simplicity of chemical synthesis on early Earth, it now appears that there may have been one or two key intermediates between the gases of the primitive atmosphere and the two essential ingredients of life, the proteins and the nucleic acids. A logical chemical cornerstone, says the University of Houston's Dr. Oro, is hydrogen cyanide, a compound found in just about every experiment aimed at preparing organic substances from the primordial reducing atmosphere. Dr. Oro, considered to be one of the foremost theoreticians in the chemical evolution field, holds that many building blocks for life chemicals—including cyanide—were deposited on the Earth when our planet was bombarded by extraterrestrial visitors, such as the comets and meteorites.

In his laboratory in Houston, Dr. Oro showed that when hydrogen cyanide and ammonia were dissolved in water and heated, amino acids were produced. But perhaps even more significant, in addition to these protein building blocks, *adenine*—one of the most important chemical components of nucleic acid molecules—was also formed.

Three years later, Dr. Cyril Ponnamperuma's group at the National Aeronautics and Space Administration's laboratories at Moffett Field, California, in conjunction with Nobel Laureate Melvin Calvin at Berkeley, also plucked adenine from a simulated early atmosphere. The reducing gases were energized by an electron beam from the Lawrence Radiation Laboratory's linear accelerator. These atomic particles mimicked ionizing radiation from potassium 40, an element found in great abundance on the ancient Earth, says Dr. Ponnamperuma. But adenine is only one-third of the typical nucleotide unit—the base. The linkup of the base with a sugar, then a phosphate, still lay ahead.

From earlier experiments with irradiated atmospheres, Dr. Ponnamperuma knew that large quantities of formaldehyde were formed, indicating that it was probably another key intermediate in the synthesis of organic substances. Although it has no sugary qualities for the layman's tongue, formaldehyde is the simplest sugar in the chemical order of things. Its probable importance in the evolution of life chemicals was again fortified when the NASA group treated formaldehyde with ultraviolet light—simulating sunlight. In this laboratory re-creation of the ancient world's surroundings, several sugars were formed, including the biochemically important *ribose* and *deoxyribose*. Ribose is the major sugar component of the RNA molecule, while deoxyribose is found in DNA.

Again using simulated sunlight, Dr. Ponnamperuma,

Fig. 6 Adjusting the laboratory reactor in which he plans to simulate primitive Earth conditions is Dr. Cyril Ponnamperuma, National Aeronautics and Space Administration, Ames Research Center, Moffett Field, California. Hypothetical components of the early Earth's atmosphere are energized by electric discharge or radiation in the upper flask where they form ingredients for life chemicals that collect in the bottom flask, a minuscule version of the primordial ocean. NASA

along with Carl Sagan and Ruth Mariner, was able to combine each of the five possible nucleotide bases with ribose and deoxyribose, respectively. The end products—two-thirds along the way to the complete nucleotide unit—are called *nucleosides.*

To set the scene for the synthesis of the complete nucleotide, Dr. Ponnamperuma moved forward from the concept of a gaseous atmosphere to a theoretical model proposed by the British physicist, J. D. Bernal, one of the oldest hands in the chemical evolution game. Dr. Bernal suggested that as simpler organic elements in nature formed from the atmospheric components, they accumulated in the waters of the primitive world, including small lagoons or the estuaries of ancient rivers. From there they could very well have seeped into the clay and soil along the water's edge or in the floor of the lagoon or estuary. Once they concentrated in the soil, they were brought into close enough contact so that they combined with one another into much larger molecules. The theory seems logical, says Dr. Bernal, because there are more organic substances found in these semiwet areas than anywhere else in the contemporary world.

In line with the Bernalian theory, Dr. Ponnamperuma believes that dried-up lagoon beds probably contained appreciable amounts of nucleosides (the sugar-base combinations) and that the third vital nucleotide ingredient —the phosphate—was probably contributed by one or more phosphorus-containing salts that were left behind when the lagoons evaporated in the hot rays of the primitive sun.

Simulating the evolution of a nucleotide unit in an ancient lagoon bed, Dr. Ponnamperuma chose sodium dihydrogen orthophosphate as a phosphate source—a salt that was probably very available in the early world. This was then heated with the nucleoside *uridine*, which is a combination of the sugar ribose and the base uracil. Dr. Ponnamperuma selected uridine because it is found only in nucleic acids of the RNA type, and RNA has been assumed to have preceded DNA in the evolution of nucleic acids.

When the NASA chemists analyzed the expected potpourri of products, they were able to identify the much-sought nucleotide—uridylic acid. Even more exciting was the discovery that some of these molecules had joined together into double nucleotides, and perhaps even into triplets.

As Dr. Ponnamperuma recently pointed out in a paper delivered to the American Chemical Society: "If dinucleotides can be formed in this process, it is reasonable to expect that several dinucleotides could be linked together by a similar process to give us the beginning of nucleic acid formation."

Even before Dr. Ponnamperuma's step-by-step duplication of what he presumes to be nature's formula for nucleotide synthesis, other research groups have built up nucleotide units (including uridylic acid) into even larger polymeric chains. For instance, Dr. Gerhard Schramm of the Max Planck Institute for Virus Research in Tübingen, Germany, reports the preparation of uridylic acid chains with total molecular weights of 10,000 or more. Under the electron microscope, says Dr. Schramm, the man-made nucleotides look very much like the naturally occurring RNA molecules to which they are chemically related. To link the nucleotides together, Dr. Schramm and other researchers use a material called ethylmetaphosphate as a catalyst. Some observers object that this material—an organic phosphate polymer—probably did not exist in the primordial soup in which so many other ingredients of life were brewed. However, in Dr. Fox's laboratory in 1962, Dr. Alan Schwartz was able to make a nucleotide polymer called polycytidylic acid using polyphosphoric acid as a catalyst. According to Dr. Fox and other researchers, this material could very well have existed in the primordial world.

## BEFORE THE CELL

In their joint attempts to clarify the chemical elements of the evolution of life, conventional biochemists and chemical evolutionists begin at the opposite ends of the same problematical log, and end at the middle. Biochemists take the organism apart, examining its components to see what makes it tick. Or they may compare similar chemicals in different species to see if they can trace that chemical to its evolutionary root. Conversely the chemical evolutionists begin before the beginning of life, re-creating chemical situations that may have combined to make the first organism live. Whether or not they will ever be able to make an organism is possibly a presumptuous, but not necessarily outrageous, question in the minds of many modern-day researchers.

As we have seen, some chemical evolutionists have traced in the laboratory what could have been the evolution of nucleic acid compounds from starting materials that may have existed on early Earth. Others have used the same starting point to chart the theoretical evolution of the proteins. Admittedly these are only components of a typical living cell and not a living cell itself, and more questions must be asked. How did these complex substances join together to the point that they were able to grow, make copies of themselves, and undergo the mutations that would push life forward to the emergence of man?

Dr. Fox believes that the proteinoids, the long chains of amino acids produced in the Miami laboratories, may have been the chemical precursors for the first living cells. When suspended in warm water which is then allowed to cool, the proteinoids aggregate into tiny spheres or globules that look very much like bacteria of the cocci type under a microscope. Through the eye of an electron microscope, the resemblance of the "microspheres" to bacteria is even more

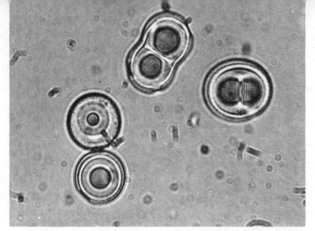

Fig. 7 Twinned microspheres. *Sidney Fox*

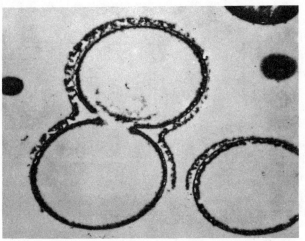

Fig. 8 Electron micrograph of double layers in microspheres.
*Sidney Fox*

uncanny. They have a double membrane, an important characteristic of living cells, they can be cut into cross sections like bacterial cells, and they keep their shape, even when "spun down" in a clinical centrifuge. Microspheres can also twin, then divide, with a provocative resemblance to cell division in bacteria and other organisms.

Dr. Fox believes that the microspheres may solve a fundamental dilemma, that is, how cells would arise in the absence of a protein when it had been believed that cells were needed in order to produce the first protein.

According to Dr. Fox, his experiments show that cells were not needed to produce protein. If the proper geological environment and the appropriate reactants were present, then the first kind of protein would arise from those conditions rather than out of the cells.

As for the first primitive cells, they would arise out of the primitive types of proteins, produced by heat from amino acids, the Florida chemist concludes.

Other researchers, including the Russian biochemist A. I. Oparin, hold that the first life forms might have evolved in the "primordial soup" from small organic droplets called coacervates. Dr. Oparin is the author of a number of books on the subject of chemical evolution which are read bible-fashion by most fellow practitioners in the field that he helped create. The coacervates, which can be easily prepared in the laboratory, are agglomerations of many different organic substances including amino acids, proteins and nucleic acids, among others. They have the interesting property of absorbing other organic and inorganic substances from a water environment, and they swell up and break apart in a manner suggesting cell division. Under the microscope they closely resemble microspheres.

Whether it was Dr. Fox's microspheres, Dr. Oparin's coacervates or some related structure that ushered in the first "living thing" will probably never be known unless somebody invents a time machine that will carry a scientist back to the era when it all happened.

## THE ATMOSPHERIC FLIPOVER

At the beginning of this chapter, it was observed that the first living thing could only have evolved from the reducing conditions of the primitive atmosphere when there was no free oxygen around. But now oxygen is 21 percent of the air around us and remains at that level, while methane and ammonia are infinitesimally small contaminants. Where did the gases of the reducing atmosphere go and where did all that oxygen come from? At what point in the evolution of life as we know it today did the atmosphere "flip over" from reducing to oxidizing?

Most chemical evolutionsts agree that there is so much oxygen in our air *because* life evolved: the bulk of it was put there by photosynthesizing organisms. In photosynthesis green plants take carbon dioxide and water from their environment and with the aid of solar energy convert it into starch which they use as food for further growth. Oxygen, the chief waste product, is then exhaled into the atmosphere.

Photosynthesis did not occur overnight; it is the result of about two billion years of chemical evolution which began when the Earth was formed four and a half billion years ago. Before the first truly photosynthetic organism emerged, say the theoreticians, large molecules called porphyrins must have been developed in the primordial soup. The porphyrins, which are related to chlorophyll in green plants and the hemoglobin in our blood, are the compounds through which sunlight works in a green plant to break water down into hydrogen and oxygen.

Porphyrin-like compounds have been prepared under simulated early Earth conditions by Dr. Anton Szutka of the University of Detroit.

If carbon dioxide is essential for the beginning phase of photosynthesis, and if it were absent in the early reducing atmosphere, how did it form? Among many answers proposed to that question, the simplest is that carbon dioxide was probably vented into the atmosphere in volcanic eruptions. A more complex argument opines that carbon dioxide was formed in two steps. In the first, sunlight reacted with water in the atmosphere to produce oxygen and hydrogen. Because the hydrogen was such a light molecule, it was not held by the Earth's gravity and escaped into outer space. Oxygen, on the other hand, oxidized methane to carbon dioxide.

As carbon dioxide was taken up by ancient photosynthesizing organisms, they exhaled more oxygen into the atmosphere. This free oxygen could then oxidize methane to carbon dioxide, and atmospheric ammonia to nitrogen, which is, of course, a major constituent of today's air.

Still later, organisms—possibly early bacterial forms—developed that could "breathe in" some of the available free oxygen and produce carbon dioxide as a waste product; just as we do, in fact. This carbon dioxide would then be taken up by other primitive plants which would give off more oxygen, continuing the cycle.

As more oxygen entered the upper atmosphere, sunlight converted some of it to ozone ($O_3$) which then formed a protective blanket against the short light waves from the sun that had energized the synthesis of the first organic substance. But at that point it did not really make any difference. Organisms were able to provide their own energy through photosynthesis, using only longwave sunlight, which could easily pierce the atmospheric blanket. Finally, the components of the reducing atmosphere, no longer having a creative function, would be reduced to their present low stature in the atmosphere.

By the time photosynthesis was well under way, with the balance between carbon dioxide and oxygen relatively stable, the primitive organisms were probably already leaving tracks in rocks, such as those discovered by Dr. Barghoorn. At that point, equipped with a full complement of cellular machinery, they entered the domain of the biochemist. Now it would be up to him to determine where these organisms and their more refined descendants fit into the overall evolutionary picture.

Which leads to the next chapter . . .

# CHAPTER 4

## CHEMICAL FOOTPRINTS ON THE EVOLUTIONARY TRAIL

Once upon a time there was a little protein, and its name was cytochrome $c$.

If that sounds like the introduction to a fairy tale, where princes turn into frogs and vice versa, the similarity is intentional. It so happens that cytochrome $c$ has a lot to do with princes and frogs and everything else that has ever hopped, slithered, swum, flown or jumped across the face of the Earth.

To begin with, cytochrome $c$ is a protein that is vital to all organisms that depend on oxygen for life, and that covers just about everything. Aside from that, Dr. Emanuel Margoliash of the Abbott Laboratories in North Chicago, Illinois, now believes that cytochrome $c$ is a significant biochemical footprint on the long evolutionary path from the simplest life form to man with all his refined complexities.

Along with his colleague, Dr. Emil Smith of the University of California in Los Angeles, Dr. Margoliash has been comparing the chemical structure of cytochrome $c$ as it exists in the cells of some twenty different species, ranging from bakers' yeast to man. From these and other

76

studies, they hope to be able to map out a biochemical chart that reflects in part the twists and turns of evolutionary history running back to the time life began.

"Obviously, this protein is very widely distributed throughout the animal and plant kingdom and is of great antiquity in evolutionary history," says Dr. Margoliash. "In fact, cytochrome c must have been present from the very moment oxygen was first used by organisms to burn their foodstuffs, to obtain the chemical energy necessary for life."

Cytochrome c is part of the so-called "terminal oxidation system" in all living cells. This important system removes electrons from foodstuffs that enter the cell, hooks them up to an oxygen molecule, and ultimately manufactures adenosine triphosphate, or ATP, the body's chief storehouse of chemical energy.

That is how cytochrome c works in the biochemical machinery of the body, but how does it fit into the evolutionary pattern?

The answer is that any protein produced in any living cell depends directly on a double spiraled coil of hereditary material called deoxyribosenucleic acid, or DNA, for short. Found in the genes, the DNA molecule transmits all genetic information from parent to offspring. Any change in a small portion of that hereditary DNA molecule must be followed by a change in the protein—such as cytochrome c—that the cell produces. These changes are called mutations, and there have been millions of them since life first appeared.

"If this mutation results in a protein which serves the needs of the organism better," says Dr. Margoliash, "the chances of survival of the individual carrying the mutation, and of its offspring, in the open competition of nature will be greater than those of individuals with the parent type protein.

"In this way, the process called natural selection will give rise to a population differing in one protein from the parent population. Many such changes may eventually lead to a new species."

Cytochrome c is essentially similar to other proteins found in the body. Chemically, it is a long chain of smaller building blocks—called amino acids—hooked together like a long string of beads. There are only about twenty different amino acids in nature, but they can form thousands of different protein chains of varying length. As proteins go, cytochrome c is a small one, varying from a combination of 104 to 108 amino acids, depending on the species in which it is found.

More important than the length of the chain is the order in which those amino acid "beads" are hooked together. This is the real evolutionary nub of the question because each amino acid variation reflects those mutational changes that Dr. Margoliash mentioned.

At the beginning of their cytochrome c studies, Drs. Margoliash and Smith asked themselves a number of pertinent questions:

Exactly how does the cytochrome c molecule differ from species to species?

How is it the same?

What do these similarities and differences tell us about the evolutionary history of the molecule and of the species that carry it?

Was there perhaps an original cytochrome c from which all other cytochrome c's evolved in a long series of mutations?

At the outset, the two chemists found that cytochrome c variations were good biochemical backing for what generations of scientists already knew about the evolution of the species.

"Species that are relatively close to each other from the evolutionary point of view have cytochromes that are very similar," Dr. Margoliash points out. "For example, between human cytochrome $c$ and the cytochrome $c$ from one species of rhesus monkey, there is only *one* amino acid difference.

"On the other hand, in species that are further apart from each other—as the horse and the tuna fish—there are as many as twenty differences. And between the horse and the moth *Samia cynthia,* there are as many as thirty-one differences. Between the yeast cell and the vertebrates studied, which are obviously far apart in the evolutionary scheme of things, the cytochrome $c$ differences range from forty-three to forty-nine amino acids."

Even though cytochrome $c$ structures varied widely from species to species, the similarities were even more provocative. Dr. Margoliash found that throughout the entire range investigated, as much as 50 percent of each cytochrome $c$ molecule was the same. Again came the researcher's eternal "Why?"

Does the unchanged 50 percent contain the essential part of the structure that makes cytochrome $c$ do the same job in every species? Or is it merely an evolutionary remnant of that first oxygen-using organism that showed up on the Earth some two billion years ago?

"This remarkable similarity could imply that all species —both extinct and extant, both plant and animal—had at one time a common ancestral form which contained the cytochrome $c$ from which all others later derived," Dr. Margoliash explains.

"If this is true, that could mean that life on Earth

Fig. 9 The large board with colored pegs representing amino acids helps to visualize similarities and differences between the cytochrome c polypeptide chains from a number of species. These include man, the rhesus monkey, sheep, cow, pig, rabbit, dog, kangaroo, king penguin, pigeon, Pekin duck, turkey, chicken, snapping turtle, rattlesnake, tuna, screwworm fly, the moth *Samia cynthia* and baker's yeast. From left to right Drs. J. W. Stewart, E. Margoliash, C. Nolan and S. K. Chan.

originated on one unique occasion. Other investigators have reached the same conclusion on the basis of several different lines of evidence, but this is the first time, as far as I am aware, that the evidence is so direct."

The next question is: If there was indeed a primitive cytochrome *c* molecule that helped usher in the first oxygen-using life form, what did it look like? How were *its* amino acids arranged? Or as the chemists put it, what was its primary structure?

"I think that when we will have a much larger number of primary structures worked out for cytochrome *c*—perhaps five or ten times as many as we have now—then we will be able to take a pretty good guess as to what was in fact the amino acid sequence of that primordial cytochrome *c*.

"At this point, it seems very likely that the portions of

the structure that have been retained over roughly two billion years must certainly have occurred in the primordial protein," Dr. Margoliash concludes.

For the future, Dr. Margoliash plans to study many more cytochrome $c$'s in many different species to fill in the blank spaces between what is known and not known about its evolutionary history. There are a few minor obstacles such as the fact that tissue containing enough cytochrome $c$ to carry out this delicate detective work is not always easy to come by in all species of interest.

Solving other aspects of the problem—such as determining the sequence of all those many amino acid chains —is not nearly as difficult as it was even five years ago. Automated analyzers can now help do a sequence determination in a matter of weeks, or months at the most. With these machines, the proteins are broken down into smaller peptide chains which can then be quickly identified by the pattern that a pen draws mechanically on a graph. These peptides in turn are then broken into smaller fragments to determine how their amino acids are hooked together. Before the development of these modern techniques chemists have labored over the same problem for years.

Another aspect of the work that makes the project a little more appealing to the chemists who have to carry it out is that many of the cytochrome $c$'s can be purified into a beautiful crystalline form. This may eventually make it possible, by the technique of x-ray crystallography, to determine the exact way in which the amino acid chain of the protein is folded in space. In turn, this would clarify the role of each amino acid in the chain and therefore the importance of the evolutionary variations of amino acids.

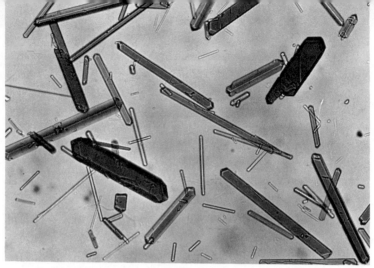

Fig. 10 Crystals of cytochrome c isolated from horse hearts photographed at a magnification of 100 times normal. *E. Margoliash*

As Dr. Margoliash and his colleagues dig deeper and deeper into the evolutionary development of the cytochrome *c* molecule, other researchers are looking for similar clues in the millions of other proteins that have evolved since cytochrome *c* first appeared. Some are comparing protein variations in egg albumin, milk, muscle and liver; others are isolating and characterizing proteins from tears, plant seeds, snake venom and blood serum.

Interest in proteins is high because they are very prevalent and so much a part of our daily life; we could not think, move, see, hear or reproduce without proteins. Isaac Asimov, American biochemist and prolific author of many books on science fiction and science fact, has this to say about proteins:

"If anything in our finite material universe can be said to approach the infinite, it is the versatility of the protein molecule and through that, the versatility of life itself."

By studying those "versatile proteins," scientists are now building up a biochemical tree of life that may pinpoint evolutionary jumping-off spots even more accurately than such visible evidences as head shape, hair and eye color, and the presence or absence of a tail. In fact, activity in this area has been so feverish in the last few years, that a whole new scientific frontier—called taxonomic biochemistry—has emerged.

Almost the entire biochemistry department of Louisiana State University's School of Medicine under the chairmanship of Dr. Fred Brazda has had a long-time interest in the chemical peculiarities of species ranging from the tiny single-celled amoeba to man. However, much of the department's thought is focused on the cold-blooded world of amphibians and reptiles: snakes, turtles, toads, chameleons, crocodiles and "that highly respected citizen of Louisiana," the alligator.

"It is not only that they are so handy in the area," says LSU's Dr. Herbert Dessauer. "They also happen to be an evolutionary middle ground from which mammals and birds evolved, stuck in as they are between fish and warm-blooded life forms."

Dr. Dessauer likes to work with blood proteins from those slithery species because mixtures of the proteins can now be neatly separated by electrophoresis, a relatively new technique.

In the electrophoresis technique, the protein molecules separate because of differences in the electrical charge they carry, as well as differences in their size and shape. As they respond to an electric current, different proteins flow through various media—such as filter paper or starch gel—toward one of two electrodes.

Subtle protein differences can be detected by the rate at which they move toward the electrodes; when the current is turned off, the proteins stay where they are. Their relative positions can then be easily seen as bands when

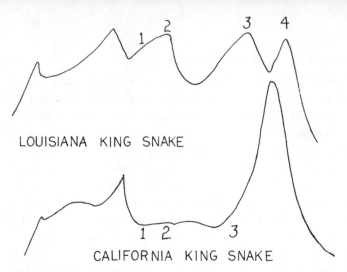

Fig. 11 The differences in blood proteins between king snakes that inhabit different parts of the United States are obvious in the two graph patterns. *Dr. Herbert Dessauer*

they are developed by special chemical dyes. In other cases, their positions can be detected by incorporating radioactive tracer elements into the original protein mixture.

Serum proteins differ not only between separate species but also within a single species. For example, Dr. Dessauer showed that there are individual differences in blood serum proteins in king snakes, water snakes, garter snakes and racer snakes, depending on where they were captured. King snakes caught in Georgia, Arkansas, Louisiana and Mississippi had similar protein patterns, but patterns were very different between king snakes caught in New York and California, respectively.

Similarly, whiptail lizards had different serum protein patterns depending on whether they lived in Arizona, New Mexico or Louisiana. And hybrids of two species of whiptail lizard had a dazzling array of mixed proteins.

To Dr. Dessauer, this suggests that in adapting to a local environment, the population accumulated genetic information that produced the observed minor differences in plasma protein.

As for the common black snake, the LSU chemist found that serum protein patterns were different in nearly every snake studied, almost as characteristic as a fingerprint.

"This means that there is a biochemical basis for individuality as well as a morphological basis," Dr. Dessauer believes. "In some cases, it is possible to get some indication about the age of the animal since certain proteins disappear from the blood of the adult, whereas they are found in the young or embryonic developmental stages.

"From certain other characteristics it is possible to detect the species. For instance, among the amphibia and reptilia, the serum proteins could tell you whether you were studying a turtle or a frog, a salamander, an alligator, a lizard or a snake."

Any zoo-going child with eyes can easily spot the difference between a lizard and a snake. Nevertheless, because both sprang from the same branch of the evolutionary tree, protein differences are not nearly as easy to detect. However, Dr. Dessauer and his LSU colleagues found that they could fill that protein gap with a protein called leucine aminopeptidase. According to one traditional criterion, the lizard has an eyelid, the snake has not. On the other hand, the blood of the snake has leucine aminopeptidase and the lizard has not.

Blood proteins are essential for the survival of man and animals. But there are other proteins that are just as essential, including those that help our muscles work, our eyes see and our hair grow. However, in the case of snakes, proteins that help make *them* survive make life difficult for other species—including man. Snake venom is such a protein, and it also occupies an important spot in Dr. Dessauer's scientific bailiwick.

In 1958, a young man from Costa Rica came to LSU to study chemistry under Dr. Dessauer. His name was Jesús María Jiménez-Porras and he had snake venom proteins on his mind.

Jiménez-Porras wanted to bring something scientifically useful back to Costa Rica after he got his degree at LSU, and he thought that a study of snake venom proteins might help. Snakebite is a big problem among Costa Rican coffee-bean pickers, causing a high toll of deaths and injuries every year. A major villain is the jumping viper, who lives a well-camouflaged life in the coffee trees and has a deadly sting.

When Jiménez went to work on various venom proteins, he found that they were as characteristic as blood serum proteins. The venom proteins distinguished one family of snakes from another or what part of the country they came from. As he continued along that basic research trail, the young scientist soon realized that his work could have some long-range medical applications.

"The jumping viper is found all over Costa Rica, which is split right down its center by relatively high mountains," Dr. Dessauer explains. "One species is found on both sides of the mountain. In comparing the venom protein from snakes caught on the west coast with east coast venoms, Jiménez found that each had different properties. From a medical standpoint, this could mean that a man who had been bitten by a west coast snake might not be protected with antivenom from an east coast viper. With this new information, accidental administration of the wrong snakebite cure would be avoided."

As they follow those protein footprints down the evolutionary trail, Dr. Dessauer and Dr. Margoliash scrutinize the chemical twists and turns from very different vantage points. Dr. Margoliash is a kind of biochemical surgeon, dissecting each different cytochrome $c$ footprint he comes across, adding up its amino acid "bones," and observing how they are held together in each species.

On the other hand, Dr. Dessauer is content to look for as many different protein footprints as he can find on that same path, meticulously cataloging this protein pattern as alligator, another as salamander, another as man. But they both realize that each different protein variation—wtihin a cytochrome $c$ molecule or a serum protein mixture—is another word, another sentence, another page in the evolutionary history of all living things. Somewhere in the past, a hereditary DNA molecule changed; when that changed a protein changed; when enough proteins changed, a species changed. Something new passed by.

# CHAPTER 5

## THE WEB-BUILDING MACHINE

Seven days a week, at about 5:30 A.M., fifty female spiders in a Syracuse, New York, laboratory begin production of their own thirty-foot skeins of near-invisible thread. Each spider lives in a glass-enclosed aluminum frame about twenty inches square. By 6:00 A.M. she will do what she has to do, create a web that will serve as her home for the day.

Six out of seven days a scientist will remove the sliding glass windows from the aluminum frame, take the spider out and carry the web to a large black box. The web is sprayed carefully with white paint, then photographed. The scientist destroys the web, and the spider is replaced in her glass case to await the morning, when she will build another web.

The Syracuse spiders are sisters to thousands of others who have been weaving their compulsive webs day after day for more than fifteen years under the observant eyes of Dr. Peter N. Witt and his associates. Dr. Witt is an M.D. and pharmacologist at the Upstate Medical Center of the State University of New York. His scientific

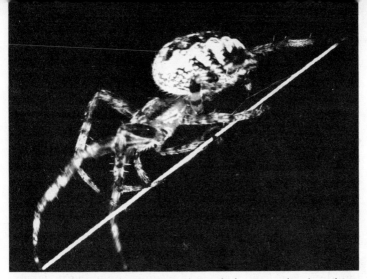

Fig. 12 The female of the species *Araneus diadematus* moving down the thread of a newly woven web. *Peter Witt*

charges—representing the females of the species *Araneus diadematus*—are also known as cross spiders because of the typical identifying mark they wear on their backs.

As a pharmacologist, Dr. Witt's main research interests center upon the effects of drugs on human beings. Unfortunately, human beings are not always the best subjects for accurate evaluation of a drug's effects because of man's variability, physiologically and psychologically. It is almost impossible to get a pure drug reaction from a human subject because its main effect may be masked by a clutter of subjective responses that have little to do with what the drug was supposed to accomplish.

On the other hand, the response of a spider is more consistent and unalloyed. Because she is instinctively driven to weaving the same type of web every day, any environmental fluctuation is mirrored by a change, ranging from mild to drastic, in the web the spider weaves. In a sense, a drug upsets the spider's inner environment.

It was in 1949 that Dr. Witt first considered the female cross spider as a screen for drugs, but since then her webs have sent their spokes and spirals into many unexpected fields, revealing valuable insights into the chemistry of the brain, synthesis of protein in the body, behavioral psychology and even the clicking, whirring world of computer technology.

### ASSORTED SPIDER LORE

Early in his spider studies, Dr. Witt found that the female cross spider's web-building machinery is extremely susceptible to climate and season. (Male spiders are not good web builders at any time.) In the winter, when temperatures are low and days short, fewer webs are woven. To counteract these variables, Dr. Witt has programmed temperature and light conditions in his laboratory so that every day is a summer day for the lady *Araneus diadematus*.

As noted earlier, the spider unreels about thirty feet of silken thread for a web big enough to fill its roughly twenty-by-twenty-inch aluminum frame. The web thread is so fine that it weighs only about one ten-thousandth of a gram—six days out of seven, that is. For a long time Dr. Witt and his colleagues were puzzled by the webs woven on Monday morning; they were a little larger and heavier than webs woven on the six other days of the week. After considerable head-scratching, note-taking and careful observation of the spider's habits, the answer was obvious. The scientists worked six days a week, but the spider worked seven. At the end of their normal workday, Dr. Witt or one of his associates always destroyed the spider's web after it was spray-painted and photographed. On Sunday night, however, no one came in to destroy the web, so the spider did it herself, by eating it. Apparently this gave her more starting material for Monday's silk production than she had any other day of the week. The outcome of the finding was that Dr. Witt never uses Monday webs in his studies.

Because he employs so many cross spiders in his research, Dr. Witt has found that it is much easier to raise his own supply than to capture them in the great outdoors. In charge of this spider nursery for several months was Miss Ricarda Baum, then a young student in Syracuse. Miss Baum became so interested in the habits of the cross spider that she has contributed two well-received papers on the subject to the scientific literature.

Among other things, Miss Baum learned that a single egg cocoon yields about 200 minuscule cross spiders. Until they can build their own webs, the spiderlings are fed on fruit flies and water, but by the time they are six weeks old, they are building their own food catchers with the best of them, says Miss Baum.

A young spider weaves a very complex web. As if trying to show off her skills, she packs the web area with tightly spaced spirals running across fine but sturdy radial spokes. As the spider gets older, its web becomes less dazzling, but only slightly less efficient. A great number of thin spirals are replaced by fewer, thick spirals. Because the open areas of the web are wider, only large flies will be caught; but the older web, for all its structural inadequacies, is better than no web at all.

Dr. Witt believes that the older spiders weave a thicker web because they "feel heavier" and need stronger threads to support their own weight. Strong backing for his belief derives from a series of experiments in which

Fig. 14 Web built by an old cross spider.
Peter Witt

Fig. 13 Web built by a young
cross spider. *Peter Witt*

he placed small weights on the backs of young spiders. Slowed by the added weight, the young spiders soon fell into the energy-conserving habits of their elders; they wove webs with fewer, thicker strands.

The cross spider sits in the center of her web waiting patiently for an insect to blunder into her gauzelike trap. Because her eyesight is very poor, she must rely on other senses to tell her that her meal has arrived. When the fly thuds against the web, the spider is instantly alert. As the fly struggles to get free, the spider extends her two front legs and tugs at the radial threads to determine which part of the web is vibrating. Then she almost scampers toward the frantic fly, embraces it, and injects a lethal poison with her pincer jaws. In seconds, the fly is dead. With a few deft movements, like a clerk wrapping a package, the spider enshrouds the hapless fly with loops of silk, then carries it back to web center where she can feed at leisure.

So sensitive is the spider to any vibration that she

quizzically probes the air with her front legs in response to the sound of a tuning fork. In fact, if the tuning fork touches the web, the spider moves toward the shimmering tine as if it were a real catch. This phenomenom was first observed in 1880 by the zoologist C. W. Boys. In 1962, a young man with the similar-sounding name of S. M. Bays carried the tuning fork study a little further. While working with Dr. Witt, Bays proved that a tuning fork could be used to teach or condition the spider to respond to different stimuli in different ways. Previously most researchers had suspected that spiders just were not very teachable.

Young Bays placed "sweet" flies that had been treated with sugar in the spider web, then touched the web with a fork vibrating at a given frequency ($C_1$). As if it were a special delicacy, all spiders bit into the sweetened fly immediately. When Bays placed "bitter" flies, treated with quinine, in the web and then touched the web with a fork that vibrated at a different frequency (C), the reaction was different. The spiders either discarded the fly or wrapped it in a silken package, but in no case did they bite into it as they had done with the sweetened fly.

After the spiders had become throughly familiar with the routine (sweet fly, $C_1$ vibration; bitter fly, C vibration) Bays then placed a small glass bead in the web, and touched the web alternately with the two tuning forks. With the $C_1$ fork the spider was so conditioned that she bit into the glass bead, expecting that the familiar vibration meant a tasty fly. With the sounding of the C fork, the spider again did what it had learned to do, discard or enwrap the bead, just as it had done with the bitter flies.

### DRUG STUDIES

Soon after he began working with spiders, Dr. Witt realized that the web builders were uncovering subtle aspects of drug action that were not obvious when they were given to man. The drug studies included sedatives, tranquilizers, stimulants and so-called hallucinogenic drugs, among others.

In some cases, Dr. Witt compared normal webs with those built by the same spider when drugged. In others he compared webs built by a large number of drugged spiders. Although the effects were often gross enough to be seen by casual observation, Dr. Witt was not too interested in these qualitative effects. To probe the less obvious effects of drug action, he drew up a set of mathematical measurements which can be applied to enlarged photographs of the various spider webs. Carefully recorded on long data sheets are the angles between the threads that jut out from the hub of the web, thread length, distance between the spirals, overall web size, shape and regularity—the beginnings of a sophisticated computer program set up later on.

The hallucinogenic drugs have received considerable study inside pharmacological laboratories and great notoriety outside the lab walls because of their dramatically bizarre effects. These range from wild, almost psychotic hallucinations, through visions of monsters, pleasantly technicolored impressions of the surrounding world, new appreciation of paintings and music, to a feeling of being one with God. Otherwise little is known of their specific biochemical effects in the body.

Among the best-known hallucinogenic drugs are mescaline (found in the sacred cactus raised by the Peyote

Indians of the American Southwest) and psilocybin (derived from certain mushrooms). In human beings their
effects seem to be generally the same. The hallucinations
are clear evidence that the drugs are affecting the brain,
but because many subjects report a feeling of heaviness
after taking the drugs, some pharmacologists suspect that
they are also hitting other physiological centers that control the motor functions (muscle action, breathing, heart-
beat, etc.). However, when the same two drugs are fed
to spiders, the webs tell Dr. Witt that the drugs are probably not pharmacological equals at all.

With mescaline, the spiders build smaller webs with
less regularity in the spacing of the spirals: a strong indication that the spider's motor activity has been affected.
It just does not move as efficiently as it might.

When *Araneus diadematus* was fed psilocybin, the
webs were shorter, but the thread was normal width.
This could mean that the drug had somehow interfered
with the spider's silk-making glands, which other experiments have shown may be linked to brain activity.
Because mescaline apparently had no such effect, its influence on the spider's chemical machinery must be significantly different, according to Dr. Witt.

Caffeine, found in coffee, and amphetamine, the chief
constituent of many weight-reducing drugs, are both
stimulants, but their pharmacological effects in spiders
show interesting variations. A spider fed a low dose of
amphetamine is inspired to build larger webs more fre-
quently than she does when not taking the stimulant.
With low doses of caffeine, she weaves her webs on a
normal schedule but they come out smaller and much
less regular than normal. With larger doses of amphetamine, the stimulant upsets the spider's web-building drive

Fig. 15 Web of the female cross spider after a dose of the stimulant drug amphetamine. *Peter Witt*

so drastically that the usually delicately wrought web becomes a chaotic cross patch of misplaced spirals and gaping holes. As a food catcher, the web is utterly useless.

When the cross spider is fed one of the stronger barbiturate sedatives, she drowsily cuts down on web size. It becomes misshapen; spirals and radii are abnormally placed. The tranquilizer chlorpromazine, which normally calms a human being without causing sleepiness, appears to dull the spider's incentive to build webs. Some tranquilized days, when her usual instincts would prod her to build her web, she ignores the signal. Other days, on the same drug, she builds, and the web is completely normal.

### THE CHEMISTRY OF WEB BUILDING

After more than fifteen years of web watching, Dr. Witt finds himself more and more enmeshed in the biochemical, physiological and behavioral riddles that underlie the daily constructions of *Araneus diadematus*. How is the silk produced? Is there a molecular signal that tells a spider to start or stop building her web?

Some answers were relatively easy to come by. Several years ago, Dr. Witt found that if the spider does not get her normal intake of flies, she continues to build her daily webs, nudged on by the same instinctive urge found in all other female cross spiders. As the unfed spider builds, she resorts to structural shortcuts to conserve her dwindling thread supply. Gradually the threads thin out, and each new web becomes a little smaller than the last. In the process, the spider loses weight at such a rate that it seems as if she uses her own body constituents to make thread for the web.

Since 1963, Dr. David Peakall, a physical chemist, has been working with Dr. Witt to clarify some of the more sophisticated mysteries of silk production in the spider. Other chemists have shown that the spider's thread is a fairly simple protein, composed of smaller amino acid building blocks. Of these, alanine is the most prevalent. Although it was obvious that the spider must get the bulk of her alanine supply from her diet, it was not clear how long it took to build the alanine into the protein of the web itself.

Borrowing a technique from nuclear chemistry, Dr. Peakall fed the spider small amounts of alanine tagged with a radioactive carbon atom, the assumption being that the "hot" alanine would eventually be built into the thread protein. Using a radiation detector on the silk of the final web, the chemist learned that it took only twelve hours for the alanine to make the complete route from meal to web.

Throughout Dr. Witt's studies on the effects of drugs on web-building behavior, abundant evidence has accumulated that there must be a link between brain chemistry and the spider's ability to make more thread protein after it has exhausted its daily supply. Although much of the evidence is circumstantial, Dr. Witt knows that some drugs that stimulate important chemical reactions in the brain induce the spider to build bigger webs containing more protein than usual. Other drugs that inhibit the same aspects of brain chemistry appear to suppress the production of thread protein.

Although there are still many loose ends to be tied together, Drs. Witt and Peakall now suspect that their work points to two biochemical messages that tell the empty gland to start making protein again: one signal probably emanates from the brain, and the other may be more localized, residing in the silk gland itself.

The spider's silk gland is a saclike cavity surrounded by a wall of tissue in which the thread protein is synthesized. After emptying the gland, which he can do quickly by reeling the thread onto a small spool, Dr. Peakall finds that tiny globules of protein begin to accumulate in the gland wall, then empty into the gland sac.

As mentioned above, this process can be speeded up or decelerated by certain mental drugs. However, when Dr. Peakall removed the gland from the spider and treated the dissected organ with the same drugs, it reacted as if it were still attached to the spider; some drugs made protein move from the gland wall to the gland sac, while others blocked that movement.

Earlier in this chapter it was noted that Dr. Witt compares one web with another by measuring a number of radial angles and other important architectural characteristics of the webs. Since the average web has about twenty radial spokes crossing thirty spiral turns, the web is composed of 600 smaller sections, any one of which can vary from one web to another. Multiply those 600 measurements by the number of webs woven each day and it is clear that it would take a large staff of technicians and scientists days, or even weeks, just to tabulate the measurements. Interpretation of the results would take even longer.

Although his first fourteen years of web work produced hundreds of pages of useful information about pharmacology and spider behavior, the project took a dramatic leap forward in 1963 when Dr. Witt joined forces with Dr. Charles F. Reed, associate professor of psychology at Temple University. Considerably impressed by the enormous amount of paper work that went into the evaluation of even a single web, Dr. Reed suggested that the project might be streamlined with the help of the IBM computer then making its debut at the Upstate Medical Center. According to Dr. Reed's plan, certain essential web dimensions (far less than the theoretical 600) would be coded on punch cards, then fed into the computer's brain, and stored there for future evaluation. Although he knew little about computer technology at the time, Dr. Witt agreed to give it a try, whereupon the cross spider stepped into the world of automation.

In the beginning, Drs. Witt and Reed were faced with the problem of translating the constituents of a many-faceted spider web into the language of the computer. As a model against which all other webs could be judged, Dr. Reed concocted a stripped-down, fictionalized master web that reflected the basic qualities of any real web that the computer would ever encounter.

With this master web lodged firmly in its electronic memory, the computer is ready to be confronted with the structural ingredients of real webs punched neatly on cards: about sixty cards for each web. Almost instantaneously, the machine can now riffle through its memory and spot differences in webs of the same spiders built before and after it has been fed a drug. It can also compare a large number of webs built by many different spiders on the same drug, or note structural abnormalities resulting from injuries to the spider, e.g., the loss of a leg.

As a remote and perhaps ultimate objective of their work, Drs. Witt and Reed hope that some day the computer's memory will hold a complete record of every variable—physiological, psychological, anatomical, etc.—that goes into the production of the ideal cross spider web. When that day arrives, the scientists expect that the machine will figuratively be in the same condition that a spider is each morning before she makes her first movement toward building a web. Primed with all the pertinent information that its memory can hold, the computer will then be asked to do electronically what *Araneus diadematus* does by instinct. With a push of a button, this properly programmed computer will begin to feed out a catalog of data, radial angles, thread length, distances between spirals, etc., until the dimensions of this machine-made web are all recorded. At that point, scientific, mathematical substance will be accorded an

ability that previously had been the unique silken re-
flection of one animal's chief function in life.

That ultimate computer web could also be the electronic answer to a question first posed nearly four hundred years ago by the philosopher Michel de Montaigne:

"Why doth the spider spin her artificial web,
Thick in one place, thin in another,
And now useth one and then another knot,
Except she had an imaginary kind of
Deliberate forethought and conclusion?"

# CHAPTER 6

## SEARCH FOR A
## MEMORY MOLECULE

How do we learn?

How do we remember?

How can it be that something outside our bodies, such as the smell of a steak or the fragrance of a rose, the sound of a violin or a thunderclap, the face of an enemy or a friend, can stimulate recognition in our minds? What happens inside the cells of the brain so that information can lodge there to be recalled time after time when needed?

These are simple questions and one day they will probably have simple answers, but the fact is that psychologists, chemists, physiologists and anatomists who have filled libraries with their detailed analyses of the structure and chemical makeup of the brain have little to report on memory and learning.

Perhaps the lack of information is not too surprising because memory and learning are usually considered abstract concepts more vulnerable to the scrutiny of philosophers than physical scientists. In the past what researchers have learned about the two processes has been almost a side dressing to what they have discovered about the operation of our nervous system in general.

As a starting point, it is known that nerve impulses are taken in through our five senses and fed through nerve fibers via electrical and chemical energy to our central nervous system, which includes the brain and the spinal cord. The operator cells that carry these messages from the senses to the brain are called neurons, and appear to be highly specialized for the job. Because of their assumed importance in making the brain function as it does, it might be useful to sketch some elementary background about the neurons.

The neuron is very much like other cells throughout our body in that it has a nucleus and a cytoplasm. The nucleus contains the chemicals that guide the manufacture of the many different substances that the cell needs to survive and thrive. The cytoplasm is a chemically rich cellular soup surrounding the nucleus.

Unlike other cells, the neurons are characterized by branching tendrils running out from the cell body, which are believed to be channels for transmitting specific impulses from neuron to neuron up the fibrous nerve path from sense organ to brain.

The neuron tendrils—known as dendrites—seem to take an impulse from an organ or another cell, then feed it into the body of the neuron. The neuron then "fires" and passes the impulse on to an adjoining cell. How this happens is still one of the blankest pages in the brain chemistry book, but it is known that the impulse leaves the cell through the axon, a long tail with a whisker-covered tip that does not quite make contact with the dendrites of another cell. Between the two cells is a microscopic gap called the synapse.

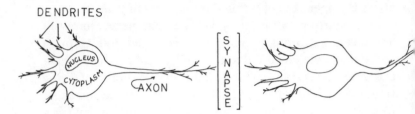

Fig. 16   Neuron Cells.

As small as the synaptic gap is, it is large enough so
that the electrical impulse, which is part of the message
from the sense organ, cannot jump the gap to the next
neuron. No one knows exactly how that important gap is
bridged, but most neuroanatomists are fairly certain that
chemicals called transmitter substances are released by
the cell, fill the synaptic area, and pass the message on.
One of the most important transmitter substances is
thought to be acetylcholine, although several other substances have been implicated as active agents in the
synaptic zone.

If you are wondering what all this has to do with
memory and learning, you are not alone, because the
scientists in the field do not know either. However, there
is one school that supposes that most answers to brain
functions—including memory and learning—are locked
somewhere in the synaptic area.

Other researchers incline to the idea that chemical
changes that take place inside the neuron after it has
been activated by some outside stimulus are the chief
bases of memory and learning. Then there are those who
believe that the two theories overlap.

## MEMORY AND RNA

If the memory of a face, an odor or a feeling can some-how be molded into the chemical matrix of the brain cell, as many scientists suspect, the molecule that fixes the millions of billions of impressions that we absorb in a lifetime must indeed be massive and versatile. Theoretically, each new impression taken in through the senses may produce either an entirely new molecule or perhaps some slight alteration in the structure of a molecule that was already there.

In the quest for memory molecules, much attention is given to the proteins and nucleic acids. Not only are they giant molecules, but when their chemical consti-tuents are shifted even slightly, the way they act in the body can change drastically. Also there is a definite con-nection between the two molecular types: ribosenucleic acid, or RNA, guides the production of the protein mole-cule from its amino acid building blocks. The end-to-end arrangement of chemical bases in the RNA molecules determines which amino acid the RNA will select from the cellular soup to weld it and other amino acids into protein molecules. Conversely, the proteins help manu-facture new RNA molecules.

Because an RNA molecule is often several thousand units long, the possible variations of arrangement of these units might easily meet the needs of a molecule that could catalog the countless sense impressions that enter the brain from birth to death. Add to this the fact that RNA is found in greater abundance in the neurons than in any other cells of the body, and its connection with learning, memory and other brain functions becomes very persuasive. There is still other circumstantial evidence.

A large buildup of RNA in the brain occurs between ages three and forty, stays fairly stable between forty and sixty, after which it begins a sharp decline. It is easy to conjecture that these chemical events reflect the concentrated diet of learning that we cram into our brains in early life, then the more relaxed intake of middle age and finally the fading memory and poor learning ability of old age.

Most modern theories linking RNA with memory and learning evolve from the work of Dr. Holger Hydén, head of the Institute of Histology at the University of Göteborg in Sweden. He and his colleagues have been able to perform such delicate surgery in brain tissue that they can separate a single neuron from the mass of cells that surround it. Using a binocular microscope and a steel thread only one-tenth the diameter of a human hair, Dr. Hydén can pluck a brain cell from the surrounding tissue with little damage to the wispy dendrites and axons that seem to be so vital for making the brain cells perform the way they do.

Once the cell is separated, Dr. Hydén and his coworkers can analyze its chemical contents, even though they often work with as little as a millionth of a millionth of a gram of material. In that almost unimaginably small amount of material they can measure how much protein, RNA and other substances the cell contains, as well as the proportions of the four bases that serve as subunits in the massive RNA molecule. As mentioned earlier, the arrangement of these bases determines what protein a cell will make and perhaps how a bit of information from the outside world is consolidated into the fiber of the brain.

The Swedish researchers have been able to show that if laboratory animals were taught a balancing trick, the proportions of the RNA bases changed significantly. Presumably this change in RNA composition was somehow related to their introduction of the new experience into the animal's brain cells.

Based on his findings, Dr. Hydén proposed a speculative theory of memory and learning in which he implicates RNA and the proteins it produces in memory and learning. To begin, he assumes that when information is relayed through our senses to a neuron, the electrical disturbance inside the cell could alter the arrangement of bases in the long RNA molecular chain. This may be only one slight change in a molecule that is thousands of units long, but it is invariably followed by a similar change in the protein it helps produce.

Continuing with the Hydén hypothesis, the newly formed protein may also be disturbed by the electrical forces in the cell to the extent that it breaks apart. The parts tie up with other molecular fragments, and an explosion of transmitter substance—such as acetylcholine—is released into the synaptic gap. When this happens, the message taken in by the cell is passed on to another neuron, then another and so on up the line to millions of other related nerve cells.

Finally, the Hydén molecular memory theory supposes that new impulse patterns will always create such an intercellular disturbance, while familiar patterns will leave the RNA and protein molecules intact. As long as they continue to be perpetuated in the cell, the memory remains. This memory of an outside impression through which we can recognize a flower by its smell, a ball by its shape or a melody by its arrangement of notes must be registered in many brain cells, suggests Dr. Hydén. How else could one account for the fact that even after surgery in which large parts of the brain are removed, memory persists?

Because flatworms, or planaria, have a very rudimentary nervous system which is nothing more than two nerve cords stretching the length of their inch-long bodies, some investigators have turned to these worms for a relatively uncomplicated look at the chemical reasons behind memory and learning. When the flatworm is cut in two, each half will grow a new head or a new tail, as most freshman biology students know. It was only recently discovered, however, that flatworms can be trained to do a number of things including running mazes, responding to light and shocks, etc. Most intriguing to contemporary researchers in brain chemistry is the discovery that when a flatworm is trained to move away from a blinking light, then cut in two, the two regenerated worms will avoid the light just as their common ancestor did.

Drs. W. C. Corning and E. R. John of the University of Rochester observed that RNA was probably behind this memory transfer when they showed that an enzyme that specifically destroys RNA molecules also blacked out the flatworm's memory. In another experiment with the intelligent flatworms, Dr. J. V. McConnell found that whatever made flatworms remember could be passed from one to another when he trained one worm, then fed it to another. In follow-up behavioral tests, the cannibalistic flatworm suggested that its ability to perform successfully a light-avoidance test might have been due to "something he et."

Of the many studies creating at least a coincidental link between memory, learning and chemical substances in the brain, some of the most provocative were recently reported by a research team from the University of California in Los Angeles.

The UCLA group, which includes F. R. Babich, Dr. A. L. Jacobson, Ann Jacobson and Susanne Bubash, was apparently able to transfer the memory of a training experiment from the brain of one rat to that of another. Obviously, the brain of a rat is more complex than the simple nerve cords of the flatworm. In the learning part of the experiment, the rats were trained to come to a food cup when they heard the click of a food pellet dispenser. As the training routine progressed, the rats became so conditioned that they never (or rarely) came to the cup without hearing the click.

When the California researchers were convinced that the rats were indoctrinated to the click of the pellet dispenser, they removed RNA from the brains of the trained rats and injected it interperitoneally, that is, into the *abdominal cavity* of rats that had never been trained to respond to the click. Then when they put the previously untrained rats (with the injected RNA) in the test cage and clicked the pellet dispenser, the rats immediately came to the food cup. Other rats that had not received the RNA injections failed to get the message from the click of the pellet dispenser.

In later experiments, the UCLA group trained rats to respond to a light flash and then transferred that memory trace to other rats. Still more recently, they reported that they could carry out the same type of memory transfer between hamsters and rats.

To the UCLA researchers, their work means that a "response tendency" can be transferred from one animal to another by injection of brain RNA or some other unidentified substance that may ride along with it in the brain tissue. Work by other scientists, including Dr. Georges Ungar of Baylor University, suggests that a protein, and not RNA, may really have been responsible.

Outside UCLA the Jacobson experiments have created considerable controversy with a number of investigators reporting that they have been unable to repeat the experiments. Aside from that, some researchers believe that it would be very difficult for RNA to move from abdominal cavity to brain without being inactivated by the body's enzymes. Also, they note that it has always been very difficult to get any foreign matter through the so-called brain barrier, a natural wall against substances that might damage the brain. Nevertheless, the UCLA findings have got many other researchers interested in the memory transfer phenomenon, and they are now busily carrying out their own versions of the work in the hope of arriving at more clear-cut answers.

### MEMORIES AND PROTEINS

More insight into the role of brain chemicals in the memory and learning processes comes from the laboratory of Dr. Bernard Agranoff and his colleagues at the University of Michigan's Mental Health Research Institute. Their work assumed that learning and memory might create new brain proteins, as several theoreticians have suggested.

The Michigan scientists wondered if the antibiotic puromycin, which is known to interfere with protein manufacture in cells, might also interfere with learning or memory in animals. They chose to work with goldfish, says Dr. Agranoff, because they are intelligent, easy to handle and inexpensive to raise.

The goldfish are trained in a long plastic container with a light bulb at either end and shocking electrodes on the sides. Blocking the middle of the tank is a hurdle which the fish do not ordinarily cross because they almost have to jump out of the water to get to the other side. In the learning routine, a fish is put in one side of the box, a light is turned on for twenty seconds, followed by a slight shock. Even an untrained fish will flip over the hurdle to the dark side when he feels the shock, says Dr. Agranoff. When the fish gets to the other side, the light is again turned on for twenty seconds and another electrical jolt is delivered. In about forty minutes, the fish learns that when the light comes on, he had better hop the hurdle if he wants to avoid an imminent shock.

After twenty trials, Dr. Agranoff separated the goldfish into two groups and injected them with puromycin in an area just above the brain. With one group the antibiotic was injected immediately after the trials; with the second, the drug was injected an hour later.

Three days later the goldfish were put back in the tank and run through the same trial to see if the drug had altered their earlier memory of the light-shock-hurdle experience. The fish that were injected immediately had compeletely forgotten what they had learned the first time around. The second group, injected an hour after removal from the tank, still remembered how to get away from the shock three days later, says Dr. Agranoff.

The Michigan results seem to verify a currently popular theory that memory is built in two phases, called short-term memory and long-term memory. From testing out human subjects, psychologists have long been aware that it is very difficult for an individual to learn something new, such as a series of nonsense phrases, if his attention is diverted for a fraction of a second. At that point, his short-term memory is very easily destroyed. However, when the subject is allowed to concentrate for even a short time, his memory is much more reliable.

Physiological psychologists interpret this phenomenon to mean that short-term memory is primarily electrical in nature. Perhaps an impulse pattern circulates for a while in a "closed loop" type of situation without really sinking in. When the brain has been exposed to the same experience for a longer period of time, the transient electrical phase gives way to permanent changes in the actual chemical composition of the brain cells, and long-term memory results.

In support of this theory, Dr. Agranoff suspects that if memory is really a process in which a new protein is formed with each new learning experience, it should be very easy to disrupt it in the early phase with a drug that interferes with protein manufacture. This is apparently what happened with the goldfish that were injected immediately after removal from the tank. In the other goldfish the memory may have already become consolidated into the brain as a new protein, which would not then be affected by puromycin.

By tagging the amino acid building block leucine with a radioactive hydrogen atom, Dr. John J. Brink of the University of Michigan could show that puromycin definitely blocks the incorporation of the amino acid into the protein of the goldfish brain. But like most brain researchers who know that their field is still only in the embryonic stages, Dr. Agranoff is unwilling to give undue weight to the Michigan findings. He points out that "there is not yet a simple correlation between the drug's action on protein and its effect on memory. Nor have specific proteins or parts of the brain been pinpointed in the little-understood memory process."

A POSSIBLE MEMORY PILL

A possible therapeutic application of the supposed RNA-memory link was foreshadowed in 1961 when Dr. D. E. Cameron of Albany Medical Center reported that he was able to improve the memory of elderly patients suffering from hardening of the arteries by giving them RNA from bakers' yeast. Later studies showed that rats fed on yeast RNA were improved performers in behavioral tests, but no one really got enthusiastic about the idea of a get-smart pill until fairly recently.

At the year-end meeting of the American Association for the Advancement of Science in Berkeley, California, a team of Chicago researchers told about a man-made chemical that appears to speed up RNA manufacture in rat brains. More importantly, reported N. P. Plotnikoff of Abbott Laboratories, the new compound called magnesium pemoline was able to make rats smarter than their brothers were in memory acquisition and retention tests. In these tests, untreated control rats and rats which had been given the drug by mouth were compared as to how quickly they jumped away from an electrically charged grid after a buzzer was sounded.

According to Dr. Plotnikoff, the rats given the drug learned to heed the warning from four to five times faster than the control rats did. In addition, the smarter rats retained what they had learned for long periods of time, while the untreated rats "failed to maintain their previously learned responses and rapidly showed a decline in performance," the neuropharmacologist said.

Dr. Alvin Glasky of Abbott Laboratories and Dr. L. S. Simon of the Illinois State Pediatric Institute carried out test-tube studies which indicate that the drug works by prodding the production of a protein that the brain cells need to manufacture RNA molecules. Dr. Plotnikoff adds that while the Abbott studies "do not definitely establish that increased RNA synthesis caused enhanced memory and learning, the experiments tend to support this hypothesis."

Chemically the Abbott drug appears to be unrelated to any of the brain-stimulating drugs now in use. On the basis of its performance in rats, the researchers hope that it may someday see use in retarded children or in presenile adults whose memory and learning ability have begun to fade.

LEARNING, HEREDITY AND ENVIRONMENT

To continue this inquiry into the riddle of memory and learning, the focus shifts back more than thirty years to the laboratory of Professor Robert Tryon of the University of California. Professor Tryon was among the first to show that intelligent rats could be selected and bred to pass that desirable trait on to future generations. Specifically he was able to breed one strain of rat that was consistently bright in working its way through a laboratory maze and another strain that was consistently dull. In other performance tests there were no such dramatic differences; in fact, the maze-dull rats were just as smart or even smarter than the bright rats.

Since Dr. Tryon's excursions into the hereditary basis of intelligence, other Berkeley researchers have been seeking for chemical clues in the brain that might be directly related to learning and memory. In the mid-fifties, Dr. Thomas Roderick (then a graduate student at Berkeley, and now at the Jackson Laboratory, Bar Harbor, Maine) was able to develop two rat strains, one of which had 20 percent more of the important brain chemical acetyl cholinesterase than the other strain did. He was working with a Berkeley research triumvirate consisting of psychologists David Krech, Mark Rosenzweig and chemist Edward Bennett; the team suspected that the high acetyl cholinesterase rats might be more intelligent than the other rats. It did not turn out to be that simple, but the chemical link was there.[*]

Careful chemical analysis of rat brain tissue by Dr. Bennett showed that the levels of acetyl cholinesterase were important to the rat's intelligence, but only when compared to another brain substance which turned out to be acetylcholine, the transmitter substance mentioned earlier. It is now known that acetyl cholinesterase and acetylcholine work in a delicate chemical interplay to transmit neural impulses. In the wake of the Roderick work, the Berkeley group was able to breed a large number of different rat families, each with subtle variations in brain chemistry. Whether or not these variations reflect the different ways that rats respond to a battery of behavioral tests is still under investigation.

This earlier phase of the Berkeley work was not too

---

[*] *Science*, Vol. 146, p. 611.

surprising from a geneticist's point of view; it stood to reason that you could breed rats with more or less intelligence. Cattle breeders and the men who compile the pedigrees of pet dogs had been breeding desirable traits into animals for centuries. What has been most intriguing about the Berkeley efforts is the more recent finding that favorable changes in the chemistry, size and general anatomy of the brain can be built into laboratory rats if they are raised in different environments.

The Berkeley group wondered what would happen if they chose brother rats from the same litter and put them into entirely different circumstances as soon as they were weaned. One part of the rat family had nothing to do but eat, sleep and look at the walls of their cages. They lived alone, had no companions, no problems to solve, just a steady diet of boredom. As for their brothers, their lives were one big challenge from dawn to dusk. They had ladders to climb, tunnels to squeeze through,

Fig. 17  Life is lively for these young rats, and their brains show it. After several weeks in this playground, the rats' brains grew larger and richer in certain brain chemicals. Siblings of these rats raised under less lively circumstances showed no such improvement. Environment had changed heredity. *Mark Rosenzweig, University of California, Science, Vol. 146*

little treadmills to operate, swings to swing on and the stimulating company of other rats. When the littermate rats entered their respective worlds, they all started out even with the same mental aptitudes and the same physiological responses. When they emerged, each group showed dramatic changes in brain chemistry, brain weight and performance.

To measure any structural differences in the brains of the different rats, the Berkeley group enlarged to include the talents of Dr. Marian C. Diamond, a neuroanatomist. With her help they learned that the cortex section of the brains of the lively rats was not only heavier but also thicker than that of their behaviorally deprived littermates. The cortex, the layered outer bark of the brain, registers most of the impulses that come into the brain through the five senses.

Appraising the chemical differences in the rat brain, Dr. Bennett found that the challenged rats were generally higher in two brain enzymes that regulate the activity and general efficiency of the brain cells. They had about 2 percent more acetyl cholinesterase than their deprived brothers did and about 6 percent more of another enzyme called cholinesterase. The distinction here is that acetyl cholinesterase, which occurs especially in the neurons, specifically controls the activity of the transmitter substance acetylcholine, while cholinesterase, which occurs especially in the glial cells of the brain, has a still poorly understood function.

Although the chemical changes in the brain of the behaviorally enriched rats were significant, they could not explain the much larger increase in brain weight. Something else had changed, and it was Dr. Diamond's job to find out what these changes were. Perhaps the number of brain cells had increased in the challenged rats.

Until recently most interest in the brain's function has centered upon the neurons, but there is a growing feeling that the so-called glial cells may be as important as, if not more so than, the neurons. These "Cinderella cells," as Professor Krech calls them, now seem to be more than brain glue which holds the rest of the brain together, as earlier researchers believed. Every neuron seems to be surrounded by glial "satellites" and the current feeling is that these cells nourish and perhaps even regulate the activity of the more familiar brain cells.

When Dr. Diamond and her Berkeley associates counted the brain cells under a microscope, there was no change in the number of neurons, which is just what all the earlier textbooks on brain anatomy had led them to expect. It is well known that we never gain neurons, but lose them as we get older. Even a medium-sized bump on the head will destroy several thousand neurons, which are then gone for good.

After a painstaking count of the glial cells, the California team found that they had increased about 15 percent in the brains of the behaviorally enriched rats. If the glial cells were really nourishing the neurons, the brains of the enriched rats were probably "healthier" and should be more able to cope with behavioral tests than their brothers'.

To find out if environment really did influence performance as well as brain chemistry, the rat brothers from the different environments were not fed for twenty-four hours, then put into a maze designed by the Berkeley group. Once in the maze, the hungry rats were taught that if they wanted to eat, they would find their food at the end of either of two alleys. One alley was dark and the other illuminated, and eventually the rats became conditioned to expect that their food would be at the end of the lighted alley, even when the position of the alley was changed by the experimenter. When this information was inscribed in the rat's brain, the routine was suddenly changed and the rat found that the food was in the dark alley. It did not take too long for either rat, enriched or deprived, to forget his first lesson and enter the dark alley. Just when he had become accustomed to that switch, the alleys were changed again. After several such switches, the rats that led the lively lives were aware that someone was playing a game with them and in a short time chose the right alley without relying on the light or dark as a food clue. They had made a successful reversal shift, as the psychologists put it. Conversely, the deprived rats were completely stymied by the many confusing switches, and never really caught on.

In summary, the Berkeley researchers think that their work shows that a stimulating early environment not only leads to changes in the chemistry and anatomy in rat brains but also that the enriched rats are better problem solvers than their deprived brothers. Although they have worked only with rats, it is not unfair to ask if their findings might also be applied to the human situation where early cultural environments can range from highly challenging to severely impoverished. It is not really possible to make the rat to human jump, says Professor Krech, but neither can such findings be ignored: "Although scientists should be very cautious about extrapolating animal results to people, I think it would be socially criminal to assume that it does not apply. If it does apply to people, then we are crippling many children by not providing them with adequate psychological environment. It is just as criminal to deprive such a child of psychological nourishment as it is to deprive him of nourishment in the ordinary sense. If we can by chance extrapolate our results to people, then we should not take the chance of neglecting these results."

The importance of a complex environment—especially in early life—on the development of the brain was again illustrated in the Neurobiological Laboratory of the Veterans Administration Center in Los Angeles. Like the Berkeley researchers, Dr. Edward Geller and his colleagues found that the brains of infant rats raised in challenging surroundings were larger than the brains of rats spending their days doing nothing.

The increased brain weights—very obvious when the rats were only four weeks old—were accompanied by a decrease in the amount of norepinephrine, which is considered to be one of the brain's most important biochemical policemen. Although it is not clear why the lively rats should have less norepinephrine (also called noradrenalin) than their deprived brothers did, the chemical differences appeared to persist for some time after the environmental differences were removed and the two groups of rats were housed together. The suggestion, as was already indicated in the work of Professor Krech and his colleagues, is that a bigger and better brain with distinct chemical advantages can be cultivated by "lively living at an early age." As for the human condition, Dr. Geller says: "Although no direct evidence links this research to human development, there is no reason to expect the human organism to be immune to such environmental influences during the early developmental stages when biochemical systems are presumed to be most plastic."

## MEMORY AND TRANSMITTER SUBSTANCE

In 1965, Dr. J. Anthony Deutsch, professor of psychology at New York University, reported that he could effectively make laboratory animals forget what they had learned if he interfered with the production of acetylcholine in the brain. Acetylcholine, as you will remember, is the transmitter substance that supposedly carries nerve impulses from the axon of one nerve cell to the dendrites of another. Its flow is held in check by the brain enzyme acetyl cholinesterase, which the Berkeley group believes is connected with intelligence and learning ability. If the acetylcholine is not controlled by this enzyme, the transmitter will jam the synapse, and further impulse transmission is blocked.

It is now known that certain organophosphate chemicals which include a number of insecticides, drugs and "nerve gases" can cause such an acetylcholine log jam by intercepting acetyl cholinesterase before it can do its job. As a result, the entire nervous system can be shut down, and the affected individual may die a very sudden death.

According to Dr. Deutsch, if memory depends on the proper functioning of the synaptic area, a drug that clogs this system might also have an adverse effect on memory. For his studies, the NYU psychologist chose a drug called diisopropyl fluorophosphate (DFP), a well-known acetyl cholinesterase inhibitor.

In the NYU laboratory, rats were taught to avoid a shock in a Y-shaped maze by running into an illuminated arm of the Y. Although the position of the "safe" arm was changed a number of times, most rats learned how to avoid the shock in less than ten tries. At that point, the rats were removed from the maze and allowed to live with their memories for various periods of time ranging from thirty minutes to fourteen days. Then they were injected with DFP and put back into the maze to see if they still remembered what they had learned.

When the fourteen-day rats were returned to the maze, they were complete strangers to the problem. Because other, uninjected rats that had been away from the maze for fourteen days relearned the maze in less than three trials, it seemed obvious that the drug had something to do with memory loss in the injected rats.

Rats injected five days after they had learned the maze seemed less affected by the drug than the fourteen-day rats, while the memories of the three-day rats were as clear as they were the day they left the maze. On the other hand, rats injected only thirty minutes after they had mastered the maze forgot what they had learned earlier.

From these and other experiments, Dr. Deutsch concludes that as the memory of the maze test becomes instilled in the rat's brain, acetylcholine probably builds up at the synapse and reaches a plateau. At that point the older, fourteen-day memory can be destroyed by a drug which adds more acetylcholine to the synaptic area. On the other hand, younger three- and five-day-old memories have built up less transmitter substance at the synapse, and when the drug is added the extra acetylcholine will not add enough to jam the synapse.

As for the rats who were trained only thirty minutes and then injected, their loss of memory may be very much like the retrograde amnesia that occurs in human beings after a sharp blow on the head or a serious operation or accident. In this type of amnesia, things learned only a short time before the accident are forgotten, while older memories can easily be recalled. Whether or not the blow on the head reduces the acetylcholine at the synapse is still unknown, says Dr. Deutsch, but his experiments indicate that it is a distinct possibility.

### ALTERNATIVES TO A MEMORY MOLECULE

Not all researchers now working in the field of memory and learning are pinning their hopes on a memory molecule. Some argue that most experiments linking these two brain faculties with RNA and protein have yet to show that a specific learning experience caused a specific change in a specific molecule.

In an attempt to put a finer edge on chemical studies of the learning process, Dr. Lewis Petrinovich and Edward Eisenstein of the State University of New York at Stony Brook have isolated a miniature nervous system from the American cockroach. From this small mass of nerve tissue which controls the insect's two front legs, they have been able to determine which cells control the right leg and which control the left.

With this precise connection between cell and function, the State University researchers think that if they train one of the two legs to respond to a shock, they should be able to find out how that single stimulus alters the chemistry of the controlling cells. Then, still working with this educated leg, they will attempt to clarify what happens inside the specialized control cells when they administer a drug that has been shown to eliminate memory in larger, more complicated systems.

Another theory of memory and learning not necessarily tied to the idea of a memory molecule proposes that when an animal or a person learns, the stimulus that conveys the new information to the brain merely makes the nerve cell work harder and become more adept at making RNA and proteins in general.

According to Dr. Eugene Roberts, chairman of the biochemistry department at City of Hope Medical Center, the nerve cell's efficiency may be increased by "synaptic muscle flexing." He theorizes that as the connections between the nerve cells increase in strength through use, or decrease through lack of exercise, the chemical reactions that occur within those cells become more or less efficient. If the neural connections are weak, the synthesis of proteins and RNA will probably diminish. This metabolic weakness "would also be expected to result in defects in the learning process," he adds.

A hint that brain cells need a stimulating environment to develop fully may be found in the Berkeley studies with behaviorally enriched rats. In addition, Dr. Paul Coleman of the University of Maryland has found that the dendrites of kittens raised in the dark for six months were abnormally sparse and very poorly developed. The dendrites, as you will remember, are the tiny nerve whiskers or branches that are partially responsible for receiving brain messages from an adjoining nerve cell.

Earlier, Drs. D. H. Hubel and T. N. Wiesel of Harvard showed that if one eye of a kitten was bandaged at birth and the bandage removed several months later, its ability to see was severely impaired, presumably because of the

Fig. 18 Neurons from the brain of a cat, complete with tiny dendrite and axon whiskers that pass information from brain cell to brain cell. *Dr. Paul Coleman, University of Maryland*

degeneration of the visual cortex, that is, the part that catalogs information taken in through the eyes.

Based on this kind of study and others now in progress, Dr. Roberts believes that "it is quite feasible to view the brain as an information-processing computer where the use of certain channels strengthens them and the disuse of other channels weakens them. It is this relative change in information processing which will then lead to memory and recall mechanisms."

Much of the work described in this chapter has received careful scientific scrutiny at the last annual meeting of the American Association for the Advancement of Science. The researchers who presented the papers and the scientists who listened discussed their findings and argued about their long-range implications, and seemed to sense a new field in early bloom. Some were excited by the possibilities for increasing man's ability to learn and remember with drugs or improved environments; others were troubled by mixed emotions akin to the soul-searching that ushered in the atomic era.

Dr. Mark R. Rosenzweig of the University of California in Berkeley pointed up the bright side of this unnamed field when he told the assembled psychologists, physiologists, biochemists and other interested participants:

"The inescapable conclusion from this conference is that our understanding of brain, biochemistry and behavior is expanding at a rapid and increasing rate. Some of you may find this an ominous and foreboding trend while others consider it reason for enthusiasm and optimism. Personally, I am inclined to be optimistic.

"First of all, a new territory is being won for human understanding. Next, while it is too early yet to know what applications can or will be made of this understanding, we can discern some possibilities. One possible result will be better education to take advantage of the brain's 'plastic' capacities.

"It may be possible to improve our studies of how an enriched education should be planned and paced so that we can investigate effects on brain as well as behavior. Another area of possible application is in rehabilitation after injury or disease to the brain. The payoff application, if it occurs, will of course come in human behavior—greater enjoyment of intellectual and emotional capacities."

In the minds of other scientists, the feeling persisted that if they may soon be able to manipulate the chemistry and functions of the brain with scientific precision, these findings would almost certainly be exploited to political and military advantage.

Aware of this dilemma, Professor David Krech, the Berkeley psychologist who arranged the AAAS symposium, agreed with his long-time co-worker Dr. Rosenzweig that: "This grand new enterprise, this brave new science of the mind has already made some major advances and is on the verge of even more significant achievements."

But he warned his colleagues that as they prepared to enter "this brave new science of the mind" they had better not leave their consciences behind.

"Whatever our research may discover may carry with it even more serious implications than the awful, in both senses of the word, achievements of the atomic physicists. Let us not find ourselves in the position of being caught foolishly surprised, naïvely perplexed and touchingly full of publicly displayed guilt at what we have wrought."

# CHAPTER 7

## DRUG FROM A HAYSTACK

When Karl Paul Link delivered his monumental lecture before the Harvey Society on January 20, 1944, the distinguished scientist Donald D. Van Slyke remarked: "The subject was handled with scientific restraint, albeit with dramatic abandon."

Although Dr. Van Slyke was discussing Dr. Link's talk on a new heart drug that had its origin in a batch of spoiled sweet clover hay, his remark underscored the Wisconsin biochemist's atypical position in the scientific world, where his entire professional life has been bathed in that mixed aura of "scientific restraint" and "dramatic abandon."

A particularly dramatic slice in the Link life was cut one Saturday afternoon in February, 1933, when a farmer named Ed Carlson drove 190 miles through a wild blizzard from his home in Deer Park, Wisconsin. He hoped to get some urgently needed advice from veterinarians at the University of Wisconsin's Agricultural Experiment Station in Madison, but the veterinary office was closed. In sheer desperation the farmer knocked on the door of Dr. Link's laboratory in the University's bio-chemistry department and found the chemist in.

The distraught Carlson told Dr. Link that he was losing his dairy herd; his cattle were literally bleeding to death. In December two young heifers were lost; in January a favorite old cow died, followed by two others. Worst of all, Carlson's bull, the hope of future herds, was oozing blood from the nose.

Although Carlson did not want to face up to it, he suspected that the cattle had died of sweet clover disease, a sickness first noticed a decade before on the prairies of North Dakota and Alberta, Canada. As evidence, he had brought along a "disaster load" that spoke for itself; a dead heifer, a milk can containing cow blood that would not clot and one hundred pounds of spoiled sweet clover hay.

To backtrack a bit, sweet clover disease was first observed and studied by veterinarians F. W. Schofield and L. M. Roderick in the early twenties. Symptoms of the disease—apparently caused by improperly cured sweet clover hay—are a gradual thinning of the blood followed by a loss of clotting power, severe hemorrhaging and death. Later the veterinarians learned that as serious as the disease was, its course could usually be reversed by withdrawing the spoiled hay from the sick cattle's diet and transfusing new blood if necessary. That was the only advice that Dr. Link had for farmer Carlson, along with the lame hope that a better cure might develop sometime in the future.

As the disconsolate Carlson disappeared again into the blizzard to make the cold 190-mile trek back to Deer Park, Dr. Link knew that his advice was nearly useless. Carlson had no other hay to feed his cattle and little money to buy new hay. And if the biochemist did not feel badly enough, the words of his German-born assistant Eugen Wilhelm Schoeffel lowered his spirits still further. In a reminiscence in the journal *Circulation*,° Link tells how Schoeffel stormed back and forth through the laboratory, shouting:

"Vat da hell, a farmer shtruggles nearly 200 miles in dis Sau-wetter, driven by a shpectre and den has to go home vit promises dat might come true in five, ten, fifteen years. Maybe never."

Then dipping his hands into the milk can full of blood, Schoeffel continued his oration: "Dere's no clot in that blood. Blut! Blut! Verfluchtes blut! Vat vill he find when he gets home? Sicker cows. And ven he and his good woman go to church tomorrow and pray and pray and pray, vat vill dey haf on Monday? More dead cows. And if he loses his bull, he loses his seed. Mein Gott! Mein Gott! Vy didn't we antishipate dis? Vy didn't we antishipate dis?"

Carlson left the lab at four, and stung by the fate that probably faced the farmer and his cattle, Dr. Link and Schoeffel "played around with the blood" until about seven that evening. They found no real answers to the disease, and when Dr. Link decided to go home, Schoeffel grabbed him by the shoulders and loudly quoted some pertinent Shakespeare.

"Before you go, let me tell you something. There is a destiny that shapes our ends," Schoeffel shouted. "There is a destiny that shapes our ends."

Schoeffel was "a bit of a mystic," explains Dr. Link. "He was convinced that Carlson's visit was no accident;

---

° Quotations from *Circulation*, XIX, #1, Jan. 1959, pp. 99 and 100, are reprinted with the permission of Dr. Karl Paul Link and the American Heart Association, Inc.

that some greater force 'up there' had directed him to
our laboratory and that we'd better not ignore the opportunity to do something about the cattle disease."

Although he had toyed with the idea earlier, Carlson's visit—and perhaps Schoeffel's words—convinced Dr.
Link that he *must* find out what there was in the spoiled
sweet clover hay that made cattle bleed to death. Clues
were scant. Other researchers, including Roderick, had
tried with no success.

Dr. Link was no veterinarian, but he had developed a
coincidental scientific interest in sweet clover only a
month before Carlson had come to his door. At that
time, he had begun a joint project with Drs. R. A. Brink
and W. K. Smith of the University's Genetics Department, aimed at making sweet clover more palatable for
dairy cattle. The research team hoped to be able to develop a strain of sweet clover that contained less than
normal amounts of a material called coumarin. Coumarin
not only makes green clover taste bitter, but it also gives
new-mown hay its pleasant sweet smell. Nevertheless, a
direct connection between coumarin and sweet clover
disease was far from obvious.

The crux of the problem was that the biochemists were
literally flying blind; they were looking for something but
they did not know what it was. Earlier, Roderick reported
that the mysterious something in spoiled hay seemed to
inhibit the production of the blood protein prothrombin, an inexpendable element in the still poorly
understood blood clotting process. Nevertheless it was a
lead, and if they could develop a usable bioassay, that
is, a technique for measuring the effect of the spoiled
hay on the prothrombin of laboratory animals, it might
help pin down the active hemorrhagic agent.

Not only could the bioassay be used to gauge and

compare the effects of different batches of hay on the blood protein, but it could also measure the clot-blocking activity of hay extracts. Finally, the bioassay could test the activity of the unknown blood-thinning factor—when and if it could ever be isolated.

When it became clear to Dr. Link that a bioassay might help illuminate the murky sweet clover situation, he scouted his current crop of graduate students for someone to confront with the problem. At the time, a young man named H. A. Campbell had just emerged from a Link-imposed apprenticeship in carbohydrate chemistry, a kind of purgatory in which the chemist spent most of his time trying to extract crystalline sugar from tarry gunks. Campbell—known as "Campy"—throve on the challenge, and distinguished himself by his clean precise work and accurate results. Realizing that the sweet clover problem might be just as messy as carbohydrate chemistry, Dr. Link told Campbell that it was up to him to isolate the cattle-killing chemical.

Campbell had come to Wisconsin from the University of Illinois with training in chemical and electrical engineering, but when he made the switch to agricultural chemistry he could never shake one remnant of his engineering background. He believed that you could not really appraise a problem until you could "put numbers on it," at which point it becomes less abstract and more measurable. Thus the bioassay could convert a vague idea —that spoiled sweet clover did something to the blood-clotting mechanism—into a concrete, scientific reality.

Campbell's bioassay began when he fed laboratory rabbits on fifty-gram servings of spoiled sweet clover hay. After a short time he measured the effect on clotting time from a single dose. This in turn was a measure of the extent to which prothrombin production had been altered in the rabbit's blood.

After about six months, Campbell felt confident that his bioassay was in good working order. Rabbits fed on spoiled hay showed average clotting times of about fifty seconds; rabbits fed on normal hay had clotting times somewhere in the area of twenty-five seconds. Now he was ready to attack the isolation problem.

As soon as he began the isolation work, Campbell and Dr. Link knew that his successful apprenticeship in the carbohydrate purgatory would stand him in good stead. Exploiting earlier discoveries by Schoeffel and W. L. Roberts, Campbell found that if he treated the spoiled hay with diluted base, he could remove most of the hemorrhagic factor from the rest of the hay. However, not only did the extraction remove the elusive factor, but the resulting sludge contained an unknown number of other factors, including chemical fragments of the plant substance chlorophyll as well as miscellaneous chemicals that showed no activity at all in the bioassay.

Two and a half years later, after treating uncounted bales of spoiled sweet clover hay with a combination of bases, acids and other chemical solvents, Campbell successfully extracted about *six-thousandths of a gram* of crystals that just had to be the hemorrhagic factor. He had begun the final isolation on his thirtieth birthday—June 27, 1939—but it was not until the wee hours of the next morning that Campbell pressed a bleary eye to the microscope optic and admired the few crystals he'd worked so long to isolate. Then he lay down on the laboratory couch and fell asleep; he would begin the final crucial bioassay early the next morning.

Before Campbell awoke on the 28th, Dr. Link dropped

into the laboratory to see how things were going. He was met at the door by a soldier of fortune type whom Campbell was using as an animal handler in the bioassays. The handler was obviously in good spirits that morning, nipping freely at a bottle of laboratory alcohol spiked with a layer of carpet tacks [sic]. When he saw Dr. Link, he grinned and announced solemnly, "Campy has hit the jackpot, Doc. And I'm celebrating!"

Dr. Link never mentioned his early morning visit to the laboratory, and Campbell was a cautious enough researcher not to make an official announcement to his director until the bioassay showed that the crystals were as active as he had expected them to be.

A few days later, exploiting his own flair for drama, Campbell walked into Dr. Link's office, showed his mentor the vial in his hand, and announced flatly, "This is H. A." It is only coincidental, by the way, that the code letters for hemorrhagic agent and Campbell's first two initials are identical.

Viewed from the outside, a three-year struggle with the biochemical grab bag that the sweet clover hay turned out to be might look like so much tedium, but Campbell does not see it that way.

"I never thought of the work as being tedious," he says. "I'm more of a problem solver than I am a pure researcher, and this was the problem I was committed to solve. The thrill of discovery keeps this kind of research chase exciting. I knew where I wanted to go, and as long as I knew I was headed in the right direction I was happy. Aside from that, Karl was always on the sidelines telling me to 'Go, Campy, go—you can do it'—but all this meant to me, was, 'damn it, deliver!' "

Schoeffel was working elsewhere when Campbell isolated the hemorrhagic agent, and could not contribute his personal brand of enthusiasm at first hand. But when Dr. Link sent him a wire relaying the good news, Schoeffel shot back a 200-word reply in which, according to Dr. Link, "he expressed his complete confidence in Nature, Fate and us."

Once H.A. was isolated, the Wisconsin group was eager to identify it chemically. This was really the target they had been aiming at ever since Carlson had brought his disaster load to Dr. Link's door six years before. But before they could do that, they would need a lot more material.

Once again, Dr. Link looked over his crop of graduate students, and selected Mark Stahmann for the next phase of the work. Using a streamlined version of Campbell's isolation method, Stahmann soon extracted a total of 1,800 milligrams—a little more than a third of an ounce —of hemorrhagic agent from about 70 pounds of sweet clover hay. That job took about four months.

Now things were moving at a faster pace. Another young Wisconsin chemist—Charles F. Huebner—ran the chemical analyses proving that the hemorrhagic agent was a substance with the impressive name of 3, 3-methylene bis (4-hydroxycoumarin), or dicumarol for short. Huebner was another product of the carbohydrate obstacle course.

Roughly speaking, dicumarol is a double-barreled coumarin molecule, and coumarin, as you will remember, is the substance that makes sweet clover taste bitter and smell sweet. But as the hay spoils, two coumarin molecules are gradually built into the larger dicumarol molecule.

When they'd found out just what atoms the natural dicumarol molecule contained, Stahmann and Huebner concluded that the ultimate proof for its molecular structure would be to re-create the same molecule in the lab-

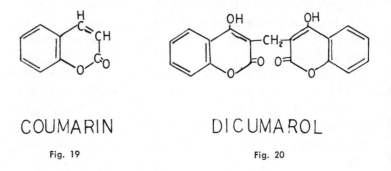

COUMARIN                    DICUMAROL

Fig. 19                          Fig. 20

oratory without the help of the hay spoilage process. By
that time, so much momentum had built up in the sweet
clover project, with all the unknowns now falling into neat
scientific boxes, that the two young chemists completed
the job only four months later. Dr. Link heard about the
synthesis on April Fool's Day, 1940. Stahmann and
Huebner had proved beyond doubt that their lab-made
material was identical with the substance that had killed
thousands of cows on the plains of the great Northwest.

As soon as the Wisconsin researchers learned how to
make Dicumarol®* in the laboratory, they began to manufacture relatively large quantities for experimental studies
in other animals. They hoped that these studies might
clarify how the material caused sweet clover disease in
cattle and perhaps lead to a more effective cure. Wisconsin University's R. S. Overman and W. R. Sullivan showed
that the man-made material seemed to work the same way
in many different species. It caused symptoms of sweet
clover disease in rabbits, rats, guinea pigs, mice and dogs.
Prior to this, the enterprising H. A. Campbell had proved

---

* Dicumarol is now a registered trade name.

that the bad effects of the blood-thinning chemical could be reversed by feeding animals Vitamin K.

As news of the Wisconsin work got out to the scientific community, medical researchers immediately felt vibration in the antennae of their imaginations. Obviously, an agent that interfered with the clottability of the blood would be no good for normal individuals, but what about people whose blood clotted too easily? There are such people, and abnormal clotting has doomed thousands of them to unexpected death when a congealed clot blocked a coronary artery. How would they respond to Dicumarol?

Researchers at the Wisconsin General Hospital and Minnesota's Mayo Clinic were the first to ask Dr. Link if he could send them some Dicumarol for studies involving human subjects. Within three months the Mayo researchers, under the direction of Dr. Edgar V. Allen, reported Dicumarol was effective in thinning the blood of patients prone to abnormal clot formation, and that the drug had no ill effects when administered properly. Other researchers reported a little later that if a patient were inadvertently given too large a dose of Dicumarol, its effects could be counteracted by Vitamin K—just as Campbell had shown in earlier animal tests.

In the next five years, Dicumarol was to see widespread use in heart clinics all over the world. Those thousands of men and women who could never be sure when the next clot would show up in the wrong place could now literally live on Dicumarol.

Just how well Dicumarol—and some of its descendants—have done since the original oral anticoagulant was first introduced is pointed out by Dr. Irving S. Wright of Cornell Medical College in New York:

"The function of these drugs is to prevent clot formation in blood vessels and veins wherever they are found in the body and to prevent clots that have already formed from extending. They are also used to prevent clots which are already formed from breaking loose from the blood vessels to which they are attached and traveling to other parts of the body. These clots may act as 'emboli' and produce rather serious consequences in the lungs, brain, or other parts of the body. These drugs are also being used for certain types of strokes.

"The anticoagulants have reduced the death rate from phlebitis to one-twentieth its former incidence. In patients with coronary heart disease—also called myocardial infarction—the death rate has been reduced between one-half and one-third. In certain types of strokes, the death rate has again been reduced one-third."

Dr. Wright, who mounted an extensive clinical appraisal of the new drug, shared the American Heart Association's 1960 Lasker Award with Dr. Link and the Mayo Clinic's Dr. Edgar Allen for their joint contributions to anticoagulant therapy.

In 1945, long after Dicumarol had been embraced by the medical profession, Dr. Link came down with a bad case of pulmonary tuberculosis, with the result that he had to spend six months in a sanitarium. While there he had little to do and to keep himself busy, went back over the history of Dicumarol and the hundred-odd chemical relatives he and his students had synthesized since the original had been isolated by Campbell. He thought that maybe one of those other untested materials might be even more effective than Dicumarol.

As the chemist pored over the laboratory data, he kept the rest of his brain active by reading everything he could find on the subject of rodent control from ancient to modern times. As he read, another switch clicked on, prodding him to reconsider an idea he had had a couple of years before. Why would not Dicumarol or one of its chemical cousins make a good rat poison? If it were added to grain, the rat would feed, wander away, come back again with friends, perhaps; they too would feed and return until they eventually died of a rodent version of sweet clover disease. Doses would be adjusted so as to be completely harmless to human beings—even children.

When he left the sanitarium, Dr. Link was eager to check out the ideas he had hatched in the hospital, and called upon the talents of L. D. Scheel, a Wisconsin chemist who had just returned from a stint in the service. When Scheel tested a number of likely Dicumarol cousins in rats, mice and dogs, he and Dr. Link found that two of them were much more potent than Dicumarol in the rat and dog. Dr. Link recommended testing one as a rat-killer. Shortly after, the material was on the market with an enthusiastic billing as the safest rodenticide known. Dr. Link dubbed the new material warfarin. The name combined the first letters of Wisconsin Alumni Research Foundation, which promoted the new material, and the last four letters of the word "coumarin." Since then, the Foundation has been enriched in royalties to the tune of several million dollars, much to the benefit of the University's research programs.

As for the safety of the new rodenticide, there have been no known human fatalities. One incident speaks for itself. In 1951, a young sailor, discouraged with his lot, thought he would like to leave the world on warfarin. After five days of eating the rodenticide in its commercial corn-starch formulation, he decided that life was not so bad after all and went to the sick bay for help. By that time, he was suffering from the effects of human "sweet clover disease," and was restored to normal by blood transfusions and a large dose of Vitamin K.

# CHAPTER 8

## THE TINIEST FILTERS

To most chemists, the world is just one big multimolecular challenge demanding simplification and separation into individual components. Accordingly, much of a chemist's time is spent removing different molecular types from a fantastic chemical grab bag: separating a colorless, odorless, tasteless gas from the air and labeling it nitrogen; purging a foul-smelling vapor from a natural gas stream and calling it hydrogen sulfide. A chemist probes the ocean mass—a solution of thousands of different chemical substances—and extracts molecules of sodium bromide. A pharmaceutical chemist removes a heart-stimulating drug from the foxglove plant and calls it digitalis; and so on and on until everything is assigned its own molecular box on an ever-expanding laboratory shelf.

There are many ways of separating molecules, including distillation, crystallization, chromatography and electrophoresis, each of which has its own refinements and complexities. However, some chemists find that one of the most direct and perhaps simplest ways to separate molecular mixtures is with a sieve. Because the average molecule is less than one hundred millionths of an inch in diameter, the problem of finding a sieve with small enough holes to remove one molecular type and leave another behind seems almost impossible to solve. But it can be done, and is done every day in many different corners of the chemical industry.

### BARON CRONSTEDT'S BOILING STONES

In 1756, a Swedish mineralogist named Baron Axel Fredric Cronstedt took a few small crystals of a rocky mineral, placed them in a crucible and heated them up to see what would happen. As the crucible warmed, vapors curled up and away from the crystals, but they seemed otherwise unchanged. His interest piqued by this first experiment, Cronstedt heated the crystals in an open flame, watched them melt and boil simultaneously, then fuse into a bubbly glass.

Because of their peculiar behavior, Baron Cronstedt called the crystals zeolites; borrowing from two Greek words: *zeo* meaning to boil, and *lithos* meaning stone. At the time, the mineralogist had no way of knowing that the crystals, usually found in the crevices of volcanoes, would be the natural ancestors of other man-made crystals that might one day make jet travel safer, gasoline more efficient and detergents "softer."

Nobody bothered much about the zeolites until eighty-five years later, when a French researcher named Damour reported that the vapor that boiled away from the heated zeolite crystals was nothing more interesting than water. He also learned that when the crystals cooled, they soaked up water voraciously, as if there were cavities inside just waiting to be refilled. A little later, another French scientist found that the dehydrated zeolites not only had a great thirst for water, but that they would also soak up other substances, including vapors of mercury, iodine and ammonia.

In 1925, the German team of Weigel and Steinhoff encountered new peculiarities in zeolite minerals. For example, one mineral called chabazite absorbed great amounts of water, as well as methyl and ethyl alcohols. That was not too unexpected, based on the earlier studies with other vapors. What was surprising was that when acetone and benzene were vaporized, they were unable to get inside the zeolite. If there were cavities inside, it was obvious that they accommodated some molecules, and kept others out.

Then in 1930, two young researchers named Linus Pauling and W. H. Taylor used a new technique called x-ray crystallography to probe the inner workings of the mysterious zeolite crystals. Their intimate analyses of the crystalline architecture of the two naturally occurring zeolites—analcite and natrolite—showed that they were indeed porous, or riddled with tiny cavities, just as the experiences of the last 190 years had strongly suggested.

The Pauling-Taylor studies also showed that the cavities in the zeolite crystals were connected by small alleys or apertures. Apparently water and other vapors worked their way through the tiny channels and then into the larger cavities. Other molecules could not force their way into the smaller alleyways. As more information accumulated about the selective absorbing properties of the zeolites, Stanford University's Dr. J. N. McBain released a technical paper in which he became the first to dub them "molecular sieves."

It was not until 1948 that scientists of the Linde Company in Tonawanda, New York, a major supplier of industrial gases, concluded that the zeolites, with their selective pores, might have some appealing commercial applications. Researchers at Linde (a division of the Union Carbide Corporation) conjectured that the crystalline sieves might be ideal for separating oxygen, argon, nitrogen and other gases from the air around us. They had already perfected a novel gas separation technique in which air is cooled to extremely low temperatures. When the temperature is raised slowly, the individual components of the air boil off according to their characteristic boiling points.

Still, it seemed reasonable to the Linde researchers that they might one day be able to pass air through a series of zeolites, so that some gases would pass through, and others would nestle snugly in the pores of the crystals, to be removed later. On closer study of many different naturally occurring zeolite minerals, the Tonawanda group had to admit that it was not going to be that simple.

Mineralogists know zeolites as "complex silicates," combinations of silicon, oxygen, aluminum and one or more other metallic elements such as sodium, potassium or calcium. Unfortunately the zeolites were not that consistent in other respects. Depending on where, when and how the crystals were formed, pore sizes varied widely. In addition, zeolite minerals are not very abundant in nature.

Not easily balked by uncooperative nature, a Linde research group headed by Dr. R. M. Milton decided that if zeolite minerals were not consistent or abundant, they would *make* them consistent *and* abundant. By 1953, they had synthesized more than thirty different zeolites, each with its own tailor-made properties.

Basically, the master zeolite recipe calls for heating up a water solution of sodium silicate, alumina trihydrate and sodium hydroxide. After mixing, the materials assume the consistency of a goo-like gel. The gel is then crystallized under carefully controlled conditions, until it passes scientific muster. The dried crystals are then mixed with a suitable binder and fabricated into spherical beads or rod-shaped pellets.

A single crystal of man-made zeolite is only about one-thousandth of an inch across, which is smaller than the period at the end of this sentence. Nonetheless, in each of these crystals there are millions and millions of tiny cubes in which four negatively charged oxygen atoms—or ions —surround a positively charged silicon or aluminum ion. In each face of the cubes is the smaller window or aperture which empties into the larger cavities you heard about earlier (see Fig. 22). The cavities are about eleven angstrom units in diameter, while the smaller apertures are about three-and-a-half angstrom units wide. An angstrom unit is about one three-hundred-millionths of an inch long.

The channels in the molecular sieves, as in Fig. 22, can be made larger by replacing the sodium ion with calcium. This is easily done by soaking the crystals in a solution of calcium chloride. The calcium zeolites are now finding extensive use in the oil industry where they can neatly separate petroleum mixtures according to the shape of the hydrocarbon molecules they contain. Hydrocarbons are compounds of carbon and hydrogen.

Automotive engineers learned many years ago that gasoline components (such as the hydrocarbon octane in which carbon atoms are arranged in long straight chains) are extremely noisy performers in an auto engine. The straight-chain molecules ignite prematurely, throwing the cylinder out of its normal rhythm and creating an unsettling clatter under the hood. Aside from the fact that it

Fig. 21 This is what a "molecular sieve" looks like when crystallized and dried. *Linde Division, Union Carbide Corporation*

Fig. 22 Molecular model of a single zeolite crystal showing apertures and cavities which can separate chemical mixtures according to their molecular sizes. *Linde Division, Union Carbide Corporation*

cuts down on fuel economy, too much knocking can seriously damage the engine.

It is also known that hydrocarbons with a branched arrangement of carbon atoms burn smoothly and quietly. The reason is that the molecules are harder to get at. Their atoms are packed tightly together while the straight-chain molecules are easily accessible to the oxygen that burns them. An analogy is the difference in burning ability between a twig and a wooden ball. Isooctane is a good example of a branched chain hydrocarbon. Based on these facts, gasoline hydrocarbons are given a low octane rating if they are as noisy as the straight chain hydrocarbons, and a high octane rating if they purr as quietly as isooctane.

Because their physical properties—such as boiling points—are usually so close together, it is difficult to separate knock from no-knock hydrocarbons by distillation, a standard petroleum refining technique. But thanks to their different molecular bulks, "noisy" straight chain octane-like molecules slide neatly into the zeolite pores, while isooctane and its quieter brother molecules stay behind.

Although gasoline manufacturers can generally do without straight chain hydrocarbons, producers of household detergents like them just fine. They now know that the straight molecules have helped solve a problem once so serious that it threatened to put them out of business. A few years after detergents first appeared in the supermarkets, large clouds of detergent foam began to billow up in sewage disposal plants, rivers and streams. Reaction from neutral observers, conservationists and scientists was unanimously the same: puzzlement followed by a demand for immediate answers. Sanitation chemists soon discovered that naturally occurring sewage bacteria—which will degrade just about anything into nontoxic products —had no appetite for the knobby hydrocarbon molecules

Fig. 23a Model of a molecular sieve molecule shows how the octane "knock" component of gasoline passes through while the "quiet" burner isooctane is too bulky, as shown in Fig. 23b. *Linde Division, Union Carbide Corporation*

Fig. 23b *Linde Division, Union Carbide Corporation*

then used in the manufacture of most detergents (alkyl-benzene sulfonates). Although it has never been shown that these "ABS" detergents are dangerous to health, the industry was quick to attack the foam problem, and switched over to straight chain detergent intermediates. These new detergents—known as linear alkane sulfon-ates, or LAS—appear to be degraded very nicely by sewage bacteria, thus eliminating the foam problem. Again, zeolite sieves proved their worth by separating the biodegradable straight-chain hydrocarbons from the "inedible" branched chain variety.

"Total flameout" is a term that can send shudders down a jet pilot's spine. It means that his fuel is not igniting, and a sudden tragic power loss can result. Flameout has several causes, but one of the most obvious is water ac-cumulation in the jet fuel.

Total flameout has been linked with the loss of at least one military jet in the United States. When investigators inspected the wreckage of the downed craft, they found ice crystals blocking the fuel feed line. This indicated that water in the jet fuel—no problem at lower altitudes —had solidified at the frigid temperatures of the upper atmosphere.

Calculations by physical chemists show that a 10,000-gallon load of jet fuel, freed of water by conventional settling techniques, still contains enough water to form ten pounds of ice at minus 50 degrees F., a typical high-altitude flight temperature. If the fuel is run through synthetic zeolites, residual water concentrations can be reduced to one part per million parts of jet fuel. At that concentration, ice will not crystallize, even at extremely cold high-altitude temperatures, says Mr. Rolland Mays of Union Carbide.

Although molecular sieves are used extensively to remove water and undesirable gases from natural gas streams, refrigeration gases and petroleum products, they do have more selective applications. For instance, the sieves can be packed with normally toxic or corrosive materials too dangerous to ship in a free state. The chemical is held securely by the pores of the sieve, then released after it reaches its destination. Along similar lines, some zeolites have been used to dispose of radioactive waste products that accumulate in the operation of atomic power plants.

### OTHER MOLECULES, OTHER FILTERS

The hamster, like man, is a land-going animal surviving in the earth's atmosphere by benefit of his lungs; he takes in oxygen which is then fed into the bloodstream to nourish the cells. The cells then give off carbon dioxide, pass it back to the lungs, which expel it to the outside atmosphere.

A hamster cannot live under water. If he inhaled the oxygen in the water that surrounded him, he would also inhale the water, his lungs would flood and death would ensue. Unlike a fish, he is gill-less, unequipped with the biological membranes which extract oxygen molecules from the water, leaving the liquid behind. But consider the hamster in Fig. 24. There he sits in the middle of a goldfish tank, eating happily, surrounded by water on all sides. How does he breathe?

For one thing, the hamster is indebted for his underwater survival to Dr. Walter Robb, the chemical engineer peering through the goldfish tank. Dr. Robb, from the General Electric Research and Development Center

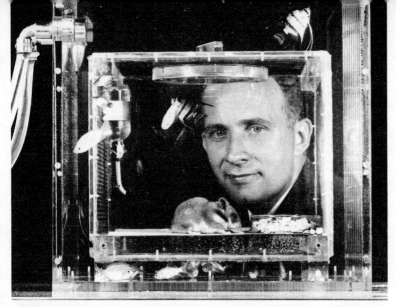

Fig. 24 This "aqua-hamster," penned in a submerged plastic tank, is kept alive by an artificial "gill"—a special synthetic membrane stretched across the top, bottom, and two sides of its underwater home. The "gill" extracts air from the surrounding water, while resisting the passage of the liquid. Carbon dioxide exhaled by the hamster passes out through the membrane, dissolves in the water, and is carried away. Without the "gill," the animal would suffocate. The membrane—an extremely thin film of silicone rubber that is also free from holes—was invented by Dr. Walter L. Robb (rear), a GE scientist. *General Electric Research and Development Center*

in Schenectady, New York, has developed an ultrathin "silicone" membrane that separates the hamster from the water surrounding him. The almost transparent membrane—which covers the top, bottom and two sides of the hamster's submerged cage—extracts oxygen from the surrounding water, just as a fish gill does, leaving the water behind. (Unlike the zeolites, the membrane has no tiny holes.)

When Dr. Robb first became involved with silicone membranes, he was not primarily interested in keeping hamsters alive underwater. As a GE employee he was well aware that his fellow scientists had used the four elements—silicon, carbon, hydrogen and oxygen—to make a wide range of silicone polymers that would stay stretchy at extreme temperatures, high and low. But what intrigued him particularly was the permeability of very thin silicone films; their ability to allow various gases to pass through their molecular network. In comparing the silicone film with other polymers, he discovered that they were about thirty times as permeable as natural rubber, and about one hundred thousand times as permeable as plastic film now used to wrap meat and other foods.

Also intriguing to Dr. Robb was his observation that different gases pass through the membrane at different rates. Oxygen moves through more than twice as fast as nitrogen does. These combined facts provoked the chemical engineer to wonder whether the silicone films might be commercially useful for separating mixtures of atmospheric gases; the same sort of question that sparked the development of the molecular sieves, as you will remember.

Air is about 21 percent oxygen, and about 79 percent nitrogen, but as far as breathing is concerned, nitrogen is essentially useless. In early experiments, Dr. Robb found that if air were forced through the membrane under pressure, or pulled through with a vacuum, the air being pulled through the membrane would be enriched to a high of 37 percent oxygen. A second pass through the membrane could increase the oxygen concentration to over 50 percent. The engineer immediately reasoned that if the oxygen content of the air could be increased just by passing it through a membrane, the silicone films might have many valuable applications where oxygen is at a premium: in hospital rooms, for instance.

Aside from the simplicity of the system and its obvious economy, the researcher points out that the membrane might add an important safety factor by eliminating the potentially explosive hazard posed by the high-pressure oxygen cylinders now used in hospitals.

Within the past few years, chemists have combined their skills with physicians and biomedical engineers to build machines that can carry out the functions of the heart and lungs while these organs are immobilized during delicate surgery. In these "artificial heart-lung machines" blood is routed past these two vital organs, and oxygen is supplied either artifically through a permeable membrane or by exposing the blood directly to air. At the same time, the carbon dioxide resulting from the blood cell's metabolism flows in the opposite direction through the pores of the membrane. According to Dr. Robb, initial reports indicate that the silicone membranes have given very encouraging results in experimental heart-lung machines. As for their value in replacing gills, Dr. Robb believes the permeable membranes will ultimately be more useful to man than the submerged hamster.

The GE researcher points out that it would be a fairly easy matter to scale up the amount of membrane area needed to meet the demands of a manned underwater station or submarine. There is plenty of oxygen dissolved in the ocean, and it could be extracted continuously by passing water through the membrane. The membrane would also return exhaled carbon dioxide to the sea. This could be done either by having the underwater vehicle move through the water like a fish, driving the water through its "gills," or by using a pump to circulate the water continuously through the membrane package, says Dr. Robb.

OLD ROCKS AND CANCER FILTERS

Scientists interested in determining the age of the universe, and researchers who wonder why a cancer cell is a cancer cell do not usually cross paths in the pursuit of their respective objectives. However, the two approaches did converge in an unexpected way in 1964, and again, the subject is filters.

Three young scientists from the General Electric Research and Development Center who work only a stone's throw from Dr. Robb, recently developed a revolutionary new method for dating ancient rocks and archaeological objects as well as meteorites and other space debris.

Drs. Robert M. Walker, P. Buford Price and Robert L. Fleischer discovered in 1963 that the radioactive element uranium leaves "tracks" in rocks and minerals that can be used to tell how old they are. The tracks are formed when the uranium atoms—found naturally in nearly all rock formations—"fission" or spontaneously split into two fragments of roughly equal size. When etched out with certain chemical agents, the fission tracks can be easily counted and the age of the rock calculated according to well-established rules of nuclear chemistry.

Although the fission tracks are produced naturally in rocks and minerals, the GE team found that fissioning uranium could also be used deliberately to "poke" holes in many man-made materials, including glass and plastics. They discovered that when uranium is placed next to thin plastic film—less than a thousandth of an inch thick —the film becomes crossed by tracks, which can then be etched to form a perforated membrane, invisible to the naked eye. The longer the plastic was irradiated, the more holes were produced. And, as they found in their rock-dating studies, the holes could be enlarged by continued

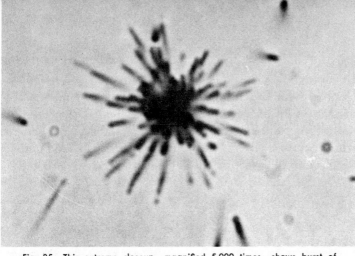

Fig. 25 This extreme closeup—magnified 5,000 times—shows burst of "fossil" tracks radiating from speck of uranium in sample of mica, a common mineral. Individual tracks in background were produced by fission fragments from single uranium atoms. Age of this specimen—one billion years—was determined by comparing ratio of tracks to total number of uranium atoms in sample. *General Electric Research and Development Center*

etching of the plastic film—up to ten microns in diameter, depending on the length of etching time. A micron is about forty-millionths of an inch.

When word of the film with the tiny holes got to Dr. Sam Seal of Sloan Kettering Memorial Institute for Cancer Research in New York, he was taken with the idea that it might be very useful to cancer researchers. Perhaps the right-sized pores could separate cancer cells—usually abnormally large—from smaller, normal cells. If they could, the plastic filters might not only help clarify differences between cancer cells and normal cells, but they might also help diagnose cancer early and detect abnormal cells in the bloodstream when they were still at a very low, perhaps controllable level.

At the Cancer Institute, Dr. Seal took blood samples from 100 patients known to have cancer cells in their blood, and in each case he was able to separate the cancerous cells on the basis of their larger than normal size.

Encouraged by his success in a field most often honeycombed with frustrations, Dr. Seal has been applying the plastic filters to more and more patients in the hope of uncovering some tiny clue that may explain what happens when cancer cells go awry and multiply so wildly that they eventually destroy the organism that carries them.

Fig. 26 Cancer cells (large dark blobs) are shown on a new plastic filter developed at the General Electric Research Laboratory. Unlike conventional filters, the new research tool consists of cylindrical holes (small white circles) with uniform diameters. Such holes do not clog easily. As a result, delicate particles—such as cancer cells—can be nondestructively filtered by gravitational action, rather than by an applied pressure. Because the filter is transparent and chemically resistant, cells can be stained and studied right on its surface, reducing the danger of accidental damage to the cells. (The section of the filter shown on this 8 x 10 print has been magnified 1,600 times.) *General Electric Research and Development Center*

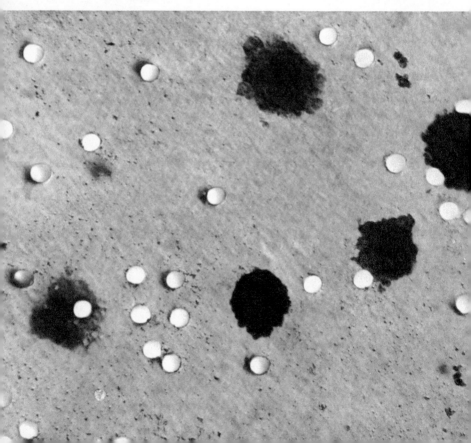

# CHAPTER 9

## HOW OLD IS IT?

The obsession with knowing how old something is or how long it endured has always been with man. He wants to know how long his species has been on Earth, and when he finds that out, he asks how old the Earth is. From there, his mind wanders out into our solar system and the elements that compose it, and he is not satisfied until he determines when these came into existence.

Biblical fundamentalists are satisfied that creation—from the first flicker of light to man—took six days, after which the Creator took a good day's rest. More liberal interpretations of the Book of Genesis suggest that the days were not really twenty-four-hour days, but only analogous days that reflect measurable periods in the formation of the stars, the planets and all they contain.

As far as the age of the Earth is concerned, one man's guess was as good as another until shortly after the turn of the century. Before then, geologists looked at the Earth rock strata and concluded that our planet was perhaps ten million, or even one hundred million years old. More

157

extreme thinkers of the day said that these estimates were too conservative and that the Earth was probably as much as a billion years old.

In 1907, a group of researchers in Cambridge, England, suggested that it might be possible to tell how old the Earth was by consulting its built-in time clock. It was a radioactive clock they had in mind, a clock that had been ticking away in almost every pebble and rock formation since the Earth first came into being.

Lord Rutherford started it all when he showed that when uranium and thorium—the two heaviest elements then known—gave off radioactivity they eventually decayed to lead and helium. He and his associates were particularly interested in isotopes or forms of the elements known as uranium 235, uranium 238 and thorium 232. The numbers after the name tell the atomic weight of the isotope, which in turn tell how many neutrons the nucleus of the isotope contains. Although these isotopes generally have the same chemical properties, the rate at which they decay to lead and helium is different in each case.

Working with Lord Rutherford at the time was an American chemist, Dr. Bertram Boltwood. It was Dr. Boltwood who proposed that if he could measure the radioactive half-life of an element, it should be possible to measure the age of the mineral that contained it. The term "half-life" means the period of time that it takes for a radioactive element to lose half of its original radioactivity through a process known as radioactive decay. Here we are referring to the primary isotopes of the elements, that is, the isotopes that existed when the earth was formed. The isotopes and half-lives that interested Dr. Boltwood are listed on the following page.

| ISOTOPE | HALF-LIFE | DECAY PRODUCTS |
|---------|-----------|----------------|
|         | (Millions of Years) | |
| Uranium 238 | 4,510 | Lead 206 and Helium |
| Uranium 235 | 710 | Lead 207 and Helium |
| Thorium 232 | 13,900 | Lead 208 and Helium |

As an example of how half-lives work, the above figures mean that it would take uranium 238 some 4,510 million years to lose half of its original identity through its radioactive breakdown to lead and helium. The same thing would happen to uranium 235 in 710 million years and to thorium 232 in 13,900 million years.

Dr. Boltwood reasoned that if he measured the amount of lead and helium in a rock or mineral, and compared those figures to the amount of radioactive uranium and/or thorium they contained, he would have a pretty good idea of how old the sample was. Using the thorium-helium approach, he found one rock sample to be about three hundred million years old, while a mineral dated by the uranium-lead method was about one and a half billion years old. This, of course, would make the earth much older than the billion-year-old guess of just a few years ago and eons older than the Biblical fundamentalist's estimate.

After more experience with the radioactive dating techniques, researchers decided that they could get very accurate dates simply by comparing the ratios of lead 206 and lead 207. Each of these was directly related to its radioactive parent, which had lost a certain amount of its substance in a given period of time. For instance, it is a fact that in a mineral known to be a half-million years old, there are 1,000 atoms of uranium 238 for every 80 atoms of lead 206. There should also be 4.5

atoms of lead 207 in the same mineral, resulting from the decay of uranium 235. Therefore, the lead 206 to lead 207 ratio in a mineral of that age should be 80 to 4.5, or more simply, 17.8 to 1. These ratios can then be used to calculate the ages of other rocks and minerals.

The lead ratio method has proved itself over and over again in dating minerals that contain radiogenic lead, that is, lead formed through the radioactive decay of uranium or thorium. However, some lead was always lead from the beginning of time, and if any of that nonradiogenic lead is present in the mineral, it can throw the age calculations wildly out of line. Fortunately, it is possible to account for the presence of this common or natural lead.

To begin, it is known that common lead contains four different isotopes, all of which existed from the beginning of Earth time but in varying proportions. The isotopes and proportions in which they now exist in an average sample of common lead are shown below.

| LEAD ISOTOPE | PERCENT | RATIO TO LEAD 204 |
|---|---|---|
| Lead 204 | 1.4 | |
| Lead 206 | 26.0 | 18.5 to 1 |
| Lead 207 | 21.0 | 15.0 to 1 |
| Lead 208 | 52.0 | 30.0 to 1 |

Knowing these values, a chemist can work his way out of the leaden quagmire by using lead 204 as a point of reference. If it is found in a mineral sample in proportions of less than 1.4 percent (and it invariably is) some of the remaining lead isotopes must be radiogenic. Therefore, the higher the ratios of the other lead isotopes to lead 204, the more radiogenic lead the sample contains.

The amount of radiogenic lead in a sample that contains thorium or uranium can then be found by subtracting the average lead isotope distribution in common lead from the total lead isotope distribution in the mineral. From this corrected lead value, the age can then be measured.

Using a combination of all the dating techniques discussed above, a mineral found in Rhodesia—called monazite—was dated at 2.7 billion years. A Canadian zircon and another rock called pegmatite were dated at about one billion years and 1.9 billion years respectively. Two other radioactive techniques indicate that a rock formation in South Africa is older than any of the previously dated rocks—namely 2.7 to 3.2 billion years old. One of these methods is based on the fact that radioactive potassium 40 decays to the gas argon 40 and the metal calcium 40. The other involves the decay of the isotope rubidium 87 to strontium 87. Values important to these techniques are shown below.

| ISOTOPE | HALF-LIFE (Millions of Years) | DECAY PRODUCTS |
|---|---|---|
| Potassium 40 | 1,310 | Calcium 40, Argon 40 |
| Rubidium 87 | 50,000 | Strontium 87 |

Unfortunately, none of the available radioactive dating techniques based on lead can give an absolute age for the Earth. The reason is that radiogenic lead in rocks is usually found to a greater or lesser extent in combination with common lead, as was discussed before. However, if there was a deposit of common lead somewhere that had the same isotopic composition as lead did when the Earth was formed, it should be relatively easy to get an absolute age. The isotopic composition of this lead could then be compared to the composition of lead formed by the radioactive decay of uranium and thorium. So far, no one has been able to find samples low enough in radiogenic lead to make these measurements possible, on Earth at least.

In the late forties, Professor Harrison Brown of the California Institute of Technology suggested that meteorites—which are presumed to have been formed at the same time the Earth was—might contain the right lead isotope distribution to help date the Earth, at least indirectly. He observed that some meteorites have two distinct phases—mineral (or silicate) and metallic. In the mineral phase are found oxidized forms of uranium, thorium, lead and other elements. In the metallic phase, however, said Dr. Brown, lead probably would not be so contaminated with the radiogenic variety.

Working in the Cal Tech laboratory—which is completely lead-free so as to avoid contamination of samples —Professor Brown's colleague, Dr. Claire C. Patterson, was able to remove a small amount of lead from the metallic phase of the famous Canyon Diablo meteorite. When this meteorite smashed into the state of Arizona like an H-bomb, it blasted an immense crater 4,510 feet wide and 575 feet deep. It has been estimated that a mass of 25,000 tons traveling at 30,000 mph would have been required to carve the crater, which was formed about 25,000 B.C.

Dr. Patterson's job was not easy, because the meteorite metal contained only one part lead per three million parts metal. Nevertheless, the Cal Tech chemist was able to analyze this tiny amount of lead, and found that the ratio of lead 206 to lead 204 was only 9.4 to 1. This was the lowest ratio ever measured, and it compares to the ratio of about 18.1 to 1, the one found in most lead

Fig. 27  Aerial view of crater, located near Coon Butte, Arizona, created when a meteorite smashed into the earth about 27,000 years ago. *American Museum of Natural History.*

deposits recently formed on the Earth. After comparing this and other lead ratios known to exist in the rocks of the Earth, it appeared that the lead in the meteorite was about four-and-a-half billion years old. If Dr. Brown's earlier suggestion was in fact true, it would mean that our Earth and the meteorite should be approximately the same age.

Recently, Dr. G. R. Tilton of the Carnegie Institution lead isotope distribution, and reports that his figures could make the Earth even older than the Cal Tech estimate, of Washington, D. C., has made new studies of the Earth's probably as old as 4.75 billion years.

To move farther back into the history of the Earth, it is possible to make an intelligent guess as to when the elements that make up our solar system were formed. Here the half-lives of the primary isotopes are excellent clues. You will remember that the primary isotopes are the elements that were present when the Earth was formed and not those that result from radioactive processes.

By considering the abundance of the primary isotopes relative to the daughter elements that they form through radioactive decay, it is possible to reach the point in the solar system's history where only the primary isotope existed. Based on the half-life of uranium 235 and its present abundance, it is estimated that the disappearance date for its daughter isotope lead 207 would be about seven billion years ago. Assuming that all the other elements were formed at that time, the elemental components of the solar system would also be about seven billion years old.

## HOW OLD IS LIFE?

Some of the deepest probings into the origins of life on the four-and-a-half-billion-year-old Earth have been made by Professor Elso S. Barghoorn of Harvard University. Using his own background as a biologist and botanist and the combined skills of chemists and geologists, he may have pushed back the dawn of life to more than three billion years ago.

In 1954, Professor Barghoorn, along with the late Professor Stanley Tyler of the University of Wisconsin, announced that there were microscopic remains of living forms in the Gunflint rock formation, part of the iron range that stretches across the northern Lake Superior region of Canada and the United States.

The tiny "microfossils" were relatively abundant in the Gunflint cherts, which are aggregates of chemical substances that precipitate from the water overlying a growing rock formation. As they form, they surround and preserve the shape of any organism that may be living

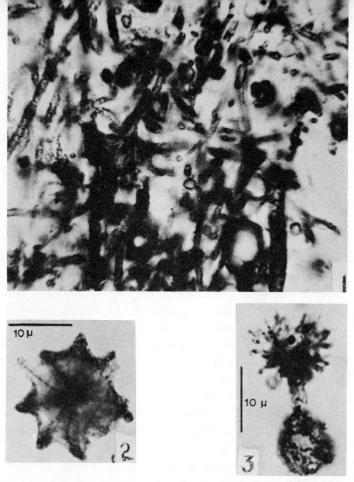

Fig. 28 Collection of organisms from the Gunflint formation. In No. 1 are algaelike filaments intermeshed with sporelike bodies. No. 2 and No. 3 are organisms unlike anything now found in nature. *Elso S. Barghoorn, Harvard University*

in the water at the time. The cherts have been dated by MIT's Professor Patrick Hurley at 1.8 billion years old, using a combination of radioactive dating techniques, including rubidium-strontium and potassium-argon.

When ultrathin slices of the chert were viewed through a light microscope—the type used in most high school and college laboratories—many of the fossil organisms looked very much like the blue-green algae that still exist in ponds all over the contemporary world. Also present were tiny microfossils that resembled the spores of very simple fungi.

The Barghoorn-Tyler findings created a major ripple in the ranks of paleontologists, who had drawn a line in time below which there was no apparent fossil record of life. Here they were speaking of conventional fossils such as shells, bones, wood or similar indicators of early life. The feeling had been that any simpler forms—including bacteria—would probably not endure through millions or billions of years of geological time. According to the line the paleontologist drew, the fossil record suddenly went blank about 560 million years ago, the beginning of the so-called Pre-Cambrian period.

Since his first peek across that line, Professor Barghoorn has looked at hundreds of thin slices of rock samples, and consistently found abundant evidence of early life. Along with the blue-green algae, he has also discovered what appeared to be "spores" produced by iron bacteria, other organisms resembling protozoa, and the previously mentioned fungal spores. Some of these organisms which Professor Barghoorn found appear to be unrelated to anything now alive.

Using an electron microscope, which can magnify things far beyond the limits of what a light microscope can do, Professor Barghoorn and his coworker J. William Schopf have discovered what appear to be fossils of rod-shaped and spherical bacteria, the two most common forms in existence today. The bacterial rods are only about a micron (about 4/100 thousandths of an inch) long and a half-micron wide, while the spheres are less than a half-micron in diameter.

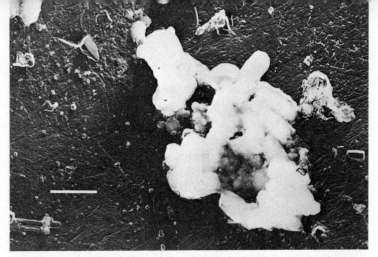

Fig. 29 An example of the rod-shaped bacteria found in the Pre-Cambrian Gunflint chert. The magnification is about x19,700. *Elso S. Barghoorn, Harvard University*

Based on their size and shape, Professor Barghoorn and Mr. Schopf have little doubt that the microfossils are bacteria, and that they were as old as the rocks that contained them. This would indicate that living organisms were already highly diversified two billion years ago. Then in 1965, Professor Barghoorn collected a sample of South African rock from the so-called Fig Tree formation, which was dated by the rubidium-strontium method as more than three billion years. Here too, electron microscopy revealed tiny bacterium-like organisms which he now calls *Eobacterium isolatum.*

Although Professor Barghoorn feels strongly that he and Mr. Schopf have been observing the oldest life forms known, even the massive enlargements of the tiny fossils give no clue as to what kind of biochemistry kept them alive in their time. The answer to that question might shed some light on the atmospheric flipover question discussed in Chapter 3. You will remember that a popular but still controversial contemporary theory has it that at an important turning point in Earth history, the composition of our atmosphere began to change from a mixture of "reduced" gases such as ammonia and methane to an oxidizing atmosphere containing oxygen, carbon dioxide and other gases. Many scientists believe that the changeover from one to the other began when plants first began to photosynthesize. Photosynthesis is the process by which plants—including algae—use carbon dioxide and sunlight to make sugars, which they then use for their own growth and nutrition. In the process, they give off oxygen—which other organisms inhale, exhaling carbon dioxide.

Using a variety of techniques, chemists have been studying the same rocks that Professor Barghoorn has been working with for any evidence of chemicals that might be related to photosynthesis. For example, Dr. Thomas Hoering at the Carnegie Institution Geophysical Laboratory in Washington, D. C., suggests that on the basis of the carbon isotope distribution in some of the rocks, the carbon was almost certainly organic carbon produced by photosynthesizing organisms.

Although the various rock formations do contain many "organic" chemicals, some researchers are not convinced that this is absolute proof that they were deposited there by living things. Many recent studies have shown that organic chemicals can be made in the laboratory without the help of living systems. In fact, this is the whole basis of the work reported in Chapter 3 in which the evolution of chemicals necessary for life was traced from the "lifeless" constituents of the Earth's primordial soup. Nevertheless, Dr. Hoering says that the carbon-containing materials produced by living things carry an isotopic marker that makes them different from nonorganic carbon compounds found in the atmosphere, rocks or the Earth's watery blanket.

The important difference revolves around two isotopic forms of carbon: the lighter form is carbon 12, and the heavier form is carbon 13. Carbon 13 constitutes about 1.1 percent of all carbon, the rest being carbon 12. In the process of photosynthesis, plants seem to be able to select carbon dioxide from the atmosphere with a relatively larger amount of the lighter carbon isotope than is contained in nonorganic substances. This lighter form is then built into the plant itself, which means that the ratio of the two forms is different in carbon-containing material derived from formerly living fossils from that of the inorganic carbonates derived from rocks.

Measurement of the carbon 12/carbon 13 ratios in rock samples from one to two billion years old indicates that some of the carbon was undoubtedly produced by living things. In fact, the ratio is very much like the carbon isotope ratios found in modern-day plants.

In addition to the carbon isotope support for the existence of life as much as two billion years ago, a different kind of chemical backing is now being built up in other laboratories. There, chemists are attempting to identify the organic compounds found in the rock samples to see if they had anything to do with what is now known about the chemistry of plants and animals. The problem is not simple, because a typical rock sample may contain only about 0.3 to 0.6 percent of organic material. This must be then extracted with various solvents, and analyzed for the presence of recognizable substances.

Working in conjunction with Professor Barghoorn, Professor Juan Oro from the University of Houston has found hydrocarbons, that is, compounds of carbon and hydrogen, in the Gunflint cherts dated at nearly two billion years old. Among these hydrocarbons were two, pristane and phytane. These compounds, in addition to being found in various bacteria, are also believed to be chemical derivatives of chlorophyll, the inexpendable element in photosynthesis as we now know it. From this evidence and that of Dr. Hoering, it is possible to theorize that photosynthesis was already under way two billion years ago.

More traces of hydrocarbons in ancient rocks have been found by Dr. Warren Meinschein at the Esso Research and Development Company laboratories and now as professor at Indiana University. He has identified pristane, phytane and other hydrocarbons of apparent biological origin in the Nonesuch shale formation of Michigan (dated at one billion years old), in the 2.7-billion-year-old rocks found in the Soudan mine in Minnesota, and most recently in the three-billion-year-old Fig Tree formation of South Africa.

Professor Meinschein argues that the hydrocarbons he found must have been produced by living things because their physical properties—such as density, arrangement of carbon atoms and refractive index (a comparative measure of the extent to which a substance bends a beam of light) —are very much like hydrocarbons of known biological origin. Like biological hydrocarbons, they also have optical activity, that is, they rotate a beam of polarized light in a clockwise direction.

In addition to pristane, phytane and other typical biological hydrocarbons, Professors Meinschein and Barghoorn and Mr. Schopf identified an organic compound called vanadyl porphyrin in the billion-year-old Nonesuch formation. This could be another significant clue to the emergence of photosynthetic life, because porphyrins are related to the chlorophyll of plants and the hemoglobin in our blood. In each case, these materials figure importantly in the photosynthetic interplay that constantly goes on between plants and animals.

The chemists who are extracting organic substances from ancient rocks are constantly challenged to prove that these materials really were as old as the rock and did not just leak into it at a later date. Along with other chemists, Professor Meinschein admits that this is very difficult to prove, but he does point out that the porphyrins were found only in the rock shale and not in the petroleum deposits found in the Nonesuch formation. The fact that they did not move from one section of the formation to another indicates to him that they did not move from some younger rock in the area. They were just too firmly bound in the original shale.

Based on the available chemical evidence, it now appears that as long as three billion years ago, rocks contained hydrocarbons which may have been produced by living things. The presence of porphyrins and the carbon isotope ratios seems to say that photosynthesis was under way a billion or perhaps two billion years ago.

In evaluating the evidence of ancient life, Professor Barghoorn points out the necessity for coordinating chemical evidence with the visual or morphological evidence. Says Professor Barghoorn:

"It is going to become more and more difficult to be dogmatic or certain that our geochemical evidence really proves the operation of such processes as photosynthesis. In other words, many of the compounds which we have in the past regarded as positive evidence of life are being shown to be capable of synthesis in purely nonliving systems.

"However, there is one saving grace. That is, if you

can find definite paleontological evidence in the form of fossils, regardless of their size, one can feel far more certain that he is dealing with fact; that is, proving life, rather than just chemical evidence to support it. On the other hand, both points of view are essential. There is confirmation by both lines of approach, the study of form and the study of organic composition," he says.


HOW OLD IS MAN?


To recapitulate as much of the Earth's history as we have covered so far, it appears that our planet is at least four and a half billion years old, and perhaps a little older. According to Professor Barghoorn's findings, the first visible signs of life were evident in rocks known to be more than three billion years old. Chemical work supporting the Harvard researcher's discoveries suggest that photosynthesis was already in progress more than a billion years ago, in an age well below the previously drawn Pre-Cambrian lines.

Above the Pre-Cambrian, the fossil record is voluminous, and we will not consider it at any length here. However, it appears to have begun when living things first developed hard shells that were not destroyed by geological pressure, temperature and the passage of time. With the opening of the Cambrian period, paleontologists have had abundant proof of the existence of tiny shellfish, sponges, oysters, snails and squids, to name just a few life forms that leaped into prominence a half billion years ago.

Between that period and the present, the dinosaurs came and went; insects, fish, birds, mammals and everything that now forms the natural history of the plant and animal worlds built their own stems and branches on the evolutionary tree of life. As for modern man, or *Homo sapiens*, he probably has not been around for more than thirty thousand years, according to most estimates. Man's ancestors—who were certainly more brutelike, but nonetheless man—have roots deeper in the past. Cro-Magnon man held forth in Europe and elsewhere about 75,000 years ago. Neanderthal man roamed Europe, Africa and the Far East 200,000 years ago, while Java man shows a fossil history that goes 500,000 years back into time.

In 1925, Professor Raymond Dart of Johannesburg described an incomplete skull and brain cast that helped solidify a train of anthropological thinking that had previously rested on theory. Careful study of the fossil—found in a limestone cave deposit in Bechuanaland, South Africa—revealed that it came from an apelike individual, but an ape with many human characteristics. At the time, Professor Dart went no further than to suggest that it was the skull of an ape with some degree of hominization; that is, a certain amount of progress toward the human state. Professor Dart called the hominid (manlike ape) *Australopithecus africanus*, which means the southern ape of Africa. Since his discovery, many anthropologists became convinced that the fossil may represent the first real proof that man descended from lower animals, as Darwin had suggested.

## ANOTHER LINK?

Since the mid-fifties, the Olduvai Gorge in East Africa has been the scene of fossil discoveries that may have uncovered still another link between the ape and man. At the same time, they may place man's ancestry deeper in the past than anyone had previously thought. The level of the gorge where these fossils were found has been dated by Drs. Jack Evernden and G. H. Curtis of the University of California at 1.75 million years. They used the potassium-argon technique, and the age has recently been confirmed by the fission track method developed by General Electric researchers and discussed elsewhere in this chapter.

The Olduvai Gorge is in northern Tanganyika, which is now part of the Republic of Tanzania. Between 1955 and the present, Professor Louis B. Leakey and his wife Mary, along with their sons and helpers, have been unearthing fossils of no fewer than fourteen hominids. The gorge was carved out by a river that cuts a path through sedimentary rocks, tuffs and lava. Tuffs are accumulations of volcanic ash that surround some of the fossil finds. The gorge has been divided into five levels, numbered as Bed I to Bed V, from the bottom of the gorge upward.

In 1959, Professor Leakey reported the discovery of parts of a well-preserved skull in Bed I of the gorge. The jaw of the skull included all sixteen upper teeth, and because the wisdom teeth were still in the sprouting stage, it is thought they belonged to a teen-ager. Professor Leakey found broken and splintered bones along with other animal fossils scattered all over the floor of the area where the skull was found, an indication that the ancient teen-ager had been using the animals as his food supply. Also present in the debris of Bed I were crudely fashioned stone tools, which was the most surprising and perhaps the most important find of all.

Anthropologist Kenneth Oakley has suggested that

about the only basis for segregating man from ape is man's ability to make tools. So, in the beginning at least, Professor Leakey's fossil find was believed to have represented a new ancestor of man, intelligent enough to make tools. At the time of the discovery, Professor Leakey called his find *Zinjanthropus bosei*. As such, he distinguished it from Professor Dart's more primitive *Australopithecus*.

Some anthropologists were not ready to accept the fact that *Zinjanthropus* was that much closer to man. They pointed out that he might still be very much an ape on the basis of his big broad teeth and small cranium. In addition, the tool evidence was shadowed by the fact that some monkeys make crude tools out of leaves and twigs to help them get their food. The controversy continued until recently, when Professor Leakey made another discovery that may make the earlier arguments a little academic.

In 1964, the Leakey party dug up a group of fossils in the same bed where *Zinjanthropus* was found. But there were enough important differences to indicate that another significant link between modern man and his more primitive hominid ancestors had been found. And the fact that this fossil was probably 1.75 million years old was even more startling. In the newly discovered fossils, the jaws contained smaller, longer teeth than those of *Zinjanthropus*. At the same time, the cranium measurements were larger. To most anthropologists, the smaller teeth are a step away from the ape world toward man, while the larger brain capacity suggests a larger brain and perhaps more intelligence. Another interesting facet of the discovery was that these new fossils—now called *Homo habilis*—were almost invariably found in the same area where *Zinjanthropus* fossils were unearthed. The new entry in the evolutionary path was named by Professors Leakey and Philip V. Tobias of the University of Witwatersrand in Johannesburg, South Africa.

From many new fossil finds acknowledged to be connected with *Homo habilis*, Professors Leakey and Tobias have constructed a picture of what this most recently discovered ancestor of man may have looked like. From the size of the bones, he probably was not much larger than a pigmy. He could stand erect, which marked another transitional stage toward man. *Homo habilis* had a cranial capacity of about 500 cc., and Java man (also called *Homo erectus*) measured about 940 cc. The value for modern man is about 1,500 cc. In balance, *Homo habilis* seems to lie somewhere between *Zinjanthropus* and our more intelligent predecessor, Java man. As for *Zinjanthropus*, he probably belongs to the same class of hominids as the fossils detailed by Professor Dart more than forty years ago. Accordingly, he is now known as *Australopithecus bosei* instead of *Zinjanthropus bosei* as Professor Leakey originally called him.

With the discovery of *Homo habilis* in the vicinity of *Zinjanthropus*, it is now considerably less certain whether the latter was the first evidence of a Stone Age culture. It could very well have been *Homo habilis* who was responsible, Professors Leakey and Tobias now point out. As for *Zinjanthropus*, now downgraded to *Australopithecus*, it is possible that he may have been an unwelcome intruder (or victim) on the home grounds of the more intelligent and perhaps more bloodthirsty *Homo habilis*. And there is more evidence for the superior I.Q. of this newly discovered ancestor of man. Near the site where his remains were found, there was a rough circle of loosely piled stones. This suggests to the two anthropologists that *Homo habilis* knew enough to come in out of the wind, and had perhaps built the stone shelter as added protection against the elements.

Of added anthropological significance is the suggestion by Professors Leakey and Tobias that two different branches of man's ancestral family were evolving side by side in the Olduvai Gorge 1.75 million years ago.

### THE CARBON CLOCK

Although the newer radioactive dating techniques have enabled scientists to trace Earth history almost to the time it began, the information they provide about man's evolution is at most indirect. If a piece of bone or a tooth were found in a rock formation of a measurable age, and if it seemed to be buried as long as the rock was, their ages were judged to be the same.

A more direct radiochemical technique for measuring the age of dead men, plants and animals is derived from the photosynthetic life cycle that they share when they are alive. In photosynthesis you will remember, plants exhale oxygen which we inhale, and they take in carbon dioxide which we exhale. The plants use our carbon dioxide to make sugars and carbohydrates which we then eat, exchanging once more the carbon atoms that mark the ticking of this so-called radiocarbon atomic clock.

As happens with many scientific developments, the route to radiocarbon dating was not very direct. Back in 1939, Dr. Serge Korff of New York University was investigating the effects of cosmic rays on the components of the upper atmosphere. He found that when cosmic rays collided with these gases, the impact of the collision sent high-energy neutrons caroming away from the nuclei of the bombarded gases. Dr. Korff learned that when these neutrons—millions of electron volts in intensity—collided with some of the gases of our own breathable atmosphere, a new elemental isotope was formed.

For example, if a cosmic neutron hit an atom of nitrogen 14 (its most prevalent form in nature), an atom of the radioactive isotope carbon 14 is formed. The most abundant natural form of carbon is the nonradioactive carbon 12. On the other hand, the radioactive carbon is continually being formed by cosmic bombardment of nitrogen 14, and when it finds its way into our atmosphere, it participates in the same chemistry that nonradioactive carbon does. This means that all of the carbon dioxide in our atmosphere contains a lot of carbon 12 and a tiny amount of carbon 14.

In the 1940's, Dr. Willard Libby, a chemist then at the University of Chicago, became very interested in radiocarbon. With two graduate students, he was able to isolate carbon 14, and found that it had a half-life of about 5,600 years. As mentioned earlier, this means that a pound of radioactive carbon will lose half of its radioactivity in 5,600 years, half of the remaining radioactivity in another 5,600 years, and so on. At the same time, concluded Dr. Libby, as the carbon dioxide is being built into plant tissue through photosynthesis, the tissue should contain measurable amounts of the "hot" carbon atoms. Then as we eat these plants, the radioactive carbon becomes part of us in a certain proportion *as long as we remain alive.*

When we die and are buried, we obviously stop taking in food and radioactive carbon. When this happens, the carbon 14 in the tissue begins to tick away the years through radioactive decay. Therefore, from the half-life of carbon 14, a five-thousand-year-old mummy would contain about half as much radiocarbon as the living, breathing reader. In the same way, the age of dead plants can be measured.

Because carbon 14 has such a short half-life, it is useful for measuring the chronology of events that took place less than thirty thousand years ago. The reason is that the concentration of carbon 14 is so low in very ancient objects that it is difficult to measure it in a radiation detector.

Before the radiocarbon clock could prove itself, it had to be tested against a wide range of objects of well-known, firmly established ages. Some of these included wood from the tomb of a pharaoh, wood from the deck of another pharaoh's funeral boat and ancient tree trunks. In most cases, the dates coincided with previous historical estimates.

Radiocarbon dating may also have upset some early ideas of when the glaciers of the Ice Age rumbled down from the north, forcing life farther and farther south. The old idea had it that the destructive frozen tide occurred more than 25,000 years ago, but fossils found in its wake show that it really rolled by less than ten thousand years ago.

The radiocarbon dating method, for which Dr. Libby was awarded the 1960 Nobel Prize in Chemistry, may also give a clue as to when the horse, bison, camel, musk ox and cave deer became extinct in the American Southwest. Driven down the face of North America by the Mankato Ice Sheet, skeletons of the animals from the Far North were found in a cave in New Mexico. Charcoal from this cave was dated at about 7,400 years.

Radiocarbon dates have also been used to trace man's progress from North to South America. Apparently early

Indians had already moved from North America to the southernmost tip of South America by 7,000 B.C.

As a chronology of man's culture, radiocarbon dating indicates that Indians in New Mexico and Mexico practiced a primitive agriculture and raised maize as early as 2,500 B.C. A Peruvian refuse heap, through radiocarbon dating, showed that the Indians had an economy based on marine foods and domesticated plants about 4,000 years ago.

According to Dr. Phil Orr of the Western Speleological Institute in California, an Indian mummy he calls "Whiskey Lil," found in Chimney Cave near Lake Winnemuca in Nevada, is about 2,500 years old. Lil's age was deduced in a number of ways: through the radiocarbon in her skin; in a bone protein called collagen; in the cedar-bark matting around the mummy.

Other events in American history as revealed by carbon dating show that:

About 9,000 years ago someone held a gigantic bison barbecue in Sage Creek, Wyoming.

Dwarf mammoths lived in Santa Rosa Island, California, more than 8,000 years ago.

Indians in what is now known as Jefferson County, New York, were operating a large crematorium about 4,500 years ago as evidenced by burnt bones, charcoal and charred leather.

And in other countries:

The linen wrappings of the Dead Sea Scrolls discovered in a cave in Palestine were shown to be 1,917 plus or minus 200 years old.

Charcoal from the Lascaux caves in France suggests that the remarkable paintings that adorn the walls were created about 15,000 years ago.

Fig. 30   "Whiskey Lil," an Indian mummy, is 2,500 years old according to the radiocarbon dating technique. *Western Speleological Institute, Science, Vol. 148,* © *1965 AAAS*

One of the most remarkable radiocarbon excursions into man's history originated in the huge Shanidar Cave in Northern Iraq, where excavations have uncovered remnants of man that go back nearly a hundred thousand years. The excavation work was supervised by Ralph S. Solecki in behalf of the Iraq Directorate General of Antiquities and the Smithsonian Institution.

According to radiocarbon dates from the top level of the excavation, charcoal ash beds and skeletons of domesticated animals were about 7,000 years old. Stone implements record that the inhabitants were representatives of the New Stone Age.

A lower excavation level dated at about 12,000 years contained bone awls used for sewing, slate engraved with primitive artwork, and many arrow heads. However, there was no evidence that these Middle Stone Age men domesticated animals or knew anything about agriculture. Piles of snail shells suggest that this was a main portion of their diet.

Another lower level of the cave was dated at about 30,000 years, with more signs of human occupation. The men who lived in the top three layers were all assumed to be members of *Homo sapiens*. However, in the lowest level of the cave, were found remains of Neanderthal man, along with stone tools and ashes from his fire. According to most age estimates—and here radiocarbon dating is not possible—this section of the Shanidar Cave was about one hundred thousand years old.

### TRACKS OF TIME

Of all the dating techniques now available, one is simple and direct enough so that you can actually "see" the passage of time in ancient rocks and archaeological objects. Called fission track dating, the technique was developed by researchers from the General Electric Research Laboratories in Schenectady, New York, who have used it successfully to date everything from glass candlesticks to ancient terrestrial rocks and mysterious space travelers called tektites.

The fission track story really begins back in England in 1959 when E. C. H. Silk and R. S. Barnes bombarded mica, used as insulation in an atomic reactor, with radioactive particles produced by the disintegration of uranium. When they looked at the mica in an electron microscope, they could see tiny tracks scattered throughout the mineral. They concluded that the marks may have resulted when neutrons from the atomic reactor split apart atoms of uranium 238, so that the fragments that were formed dug into the mica insulator. The GE researchers—including Drs. Robert M. Walker, P. Buford Price and Robert L. Fleischer mentioned in the previous chapter—wondered if the same thing might happen naturally. After all, there are small amounts of uranium 238 in almost every kind of terrestrial rock, and uranium 238 does undergo spontaneous fission.

When they looked at a piece of mica known to have uranium in it, the GE investigators saw the same kind of tracks that the British scientists noted in the mica that had been bombarded with atomic fragments in the nuclear reactor. Again, these tracks could be seen only through an electron microscope at a magnification of about 50,000.

Later, the GE team found that they could make the tracks large enough so that they could easily be seen and counted through an ordinary low-power light microscope. To get this blown-up view of the tracks, they had

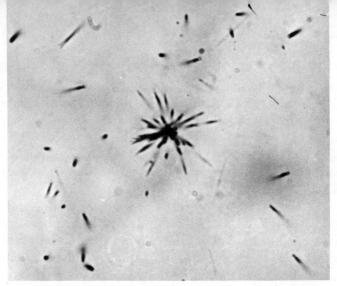

Fig. 31 Cluster of tracks radiates from a speck of uranium in a sample of the mineral biotite. *General Electric Research and Development Center*

to etch the rock or mica sample with hydrofluoric acid, one of the most reactive chemicals known. This made the tracks larger, but left the test sample otherwise undisturbed.

To use the fission tracks as a key to the age of a rock or archaeological sample, the GE scientists work with several well-documented facts. The first is that about two atoms out of every million atoms of uranium 238 in a sample will split spontaneously and leave a track in a given period of time. The more uranium there is in a sample, the more fission tracks there will be.

In the actual dating of a sample, it is first etched with hydrofluoric acid, and the enlarged tracks are photographed and counted. These tracks alone will not tell how old the sample is, because there is still no way of knowing how much uranium the sample contained. To find this out requires an additional bit of ingenious but rather simple atomic-age mathematics. First, the sample is bombarded with neutrons in an atomic reactor, so that a fraction of the uranium still present will split apart and form new fission tracks. These are again enlarged with hydrofluoric acid. Then by determining the ratio of the ancient "fossil tracks" and the new artificially produced tracks, the age of the mineral can be calculated.

Drs. Price, Fleischer and Walker believe that the fission track method may have advantages over other radio-active dating techniques, because even very small samples contain enough uranium to give an accurate date. For instance, a tiny chunk of rock that may contain only one part per million of uranium can still be traced a half million years back into the past. Rocks with larger amounts have been assigned even older ages, a little over a billion years in some cases. The scientists point out that the fission track method does not require expensive radiation detectors, and can be carried out easily and cheaply in just about any college or university geology laboratory.

In addition to dating ancient rocks, the fission tracking method has also been used to clear up some of the mystery surrounding interesting visitors from space called tektites and impactites. These glassy objects, found scattered over the face of the earth, range from pebble size to about the size of a grapefruit.

No one knows exactly how they were formed or where they came from, but one theory states that the tektites probably showered down on the Earth after some enormous celestial body blasted them off the surface of the moon. As for the impactites, they may have been formed by a similar blast on Earth. According to their fission track content, Drs. Walker, Fleischer and Price believe that the impactites may have been formed at the same time.

Their experiments show that the Earth collided with the celestial debris that formed the impactites and tektites at least three times in the Earth's past history. For instance, fission track dates showed that both the impactites and tektites that landed in the United States are about thirty-four million years old. Another glassy shower of tektites and impactites hit Europe fifteen million years ago, while Southeast Asia received the glassy invaders seven hundred thousand years ago. The tektite dates agree with earlier dates derived from the potassium-argon method.

The General Electric researchers also suspect that uranium fission tracks can tell them how long ago the tektites were first formed and when they finally arrived on the Earth. These measurements depended on the architecture of the tektites and some speculation about what happened when the tektites burnt their way through the Earth's thickening atmosphere. The tektites have an outer flange, which was apparently formed as the molten material from the front of the tektite was swept to the back portion where it eventually solidified. While it was melting, the uranium tracks that the flange once contained were erased, although the tracks in the core of the tektite remained undisturbed. Following this reasoning, tracks now found in the flange could have been formed only by uranium that fissioned since the uranium has been on Earth. Tracks inside the core, however, were there at the time the tektite was first formed. Based on this and other evidence, the GE team concludes that the age of formation and the time the tektites arrived on the

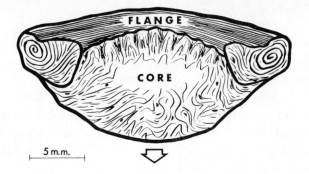

Earth were roughly the same. This means that the tektites could not have been formed far from the Earth, and certainly no farther than the Moon.

Since perfecting the fission track technique, Drs. Walker, Price and Fleischer have dated samples of man-made glass ranging in age from twenty years to volcanic glass aged at about forty million years. The method has also been used to trace the period when American glassmakers used uranium oxides to add yellow, green and yellow-green colors to glass objects. For instance, a glass candlestick which was thought to have been made in about 1850 to 1860, because of its style, was dated at 1840 plus or minus 20 years by the General Electric group and Dr. R. W. Brill of the Corning Glass Museum. They were also able to show that most American glassmakers first began to add uranium oxide to glass about 120 years ago, eventually giving up this practice around 1945 in favor of cheaper glass colors.

An important footnote to the fission track work is that the fundamental principles involved have been used to create plastic filters that may see important uses in medical research. This offshoot of the General Electric research was referred to in Chapter 8.

# CHAPTER 10

## VIRUS KILLERS

At the turn of the century, the word "virus" meant what its Latin root suggested—poison. It was coined to describe any number of mysterious substances that could make you sick, or even kill you. As recently as twenty years ago, viruses were no less mysterious in the lay and not-so-lay mind. They were blamed for terrible headaches, unpredictable stomach upsets and other symptoms that the family doctor could not quite put his finger on. All in all, the virus became a kind of sick man's status symbol, serious enough to keep him away from work, mild enough to provide sociable conversation for several days after he got back.

Since the thirties, scientists have realized that viruses are everywhere, creating havoc in plants, animals and man. In 1935, about thirty viruses had definitely been linked with human diseases. By 1965, more than a hundred were added to the list, with several hundred more in the suspicious character category. However, the virus that helped researchers break through the early haze into a clearer understanding of what viruses really are was a plant virus.

In 1892, the Russian researcher Dmitri Iwanowski was studying a very troublesome affliction of tobacco plants called the mosaic disease. Widespread through tobacco-growing regions, the disease was the cause of stunted plants and severe mottling of the leaves.

Iwanowski believed that if he squeezed the sap from infected plants and passed it through a bacterial filter, the bacteria that supposedly caused the disease would stay behind on the filter. But they did not. Whatever was responsible for damaging the plants passed through the filter pores and was able to transmit the disease to other plants as virulently as before.

The Russian scientist had no reason to believe that he was working with anything other than a bacterium, but it was up to the Dutch bacteriologist Martinus Willem Beijerinck to argue with his peers that the tobacco disease was caused by an entirely different breed of disease agent. Try as he might, Beijerinck could not get the tobacco disease substance to grow in culture media where bacteria normally thrived. He called the new trouble-maker "contagium vivum fluidum," or living fluid infect-ant. Later, when it was discovered that the material that causes foot-and-mouth disease also passed through the bacterial filter, the name "filterable virus" was introduced, which eventually was diminished to "virus."

At that point, the newly named virus was otherwise undistinguished except for its name and its ability to slip through the pores of bacterial filters. There were still scientists who clung to the idea that viruses were really only smaller versions of bacteria, perhaps the smallest living organisms of all.

In 1935, a young chemist named Wendell Stanley, then working at the Rockefeller Institute for Medical

Research in New York, convinced himself that the sap of diseased tobacco plants was worth a closer look. He proceeded to do what chemists do when they really want to find out what a substance is: he crystallized it. His conversion of a viscous sap into fine crystalline needles upset many traditional beliefs, including the concept that viruses were living substances. Although its exact molecular structure was still unknown, Dr. Stanley insisted that a virus, outside a living cell at least, was merely a collection of atoms with no more life in them than a crystal of salt or sugar. In 1946, Dr. Stanley's discovery was acknowledged internationally when he shared that year's Nobel Prize for Chemistry with Drs. J. H. Northrop and James E. Sumner. In his award address, Dr. Stanley noted: "For a time there was great skepticism that the crystalline material could be tobacco mosaic, due chiefly to the old idea that viruses were living organisms. A wide variety of experimental approaches had been used to test the proposal that the crystalline material represented tobacco mosaic virus. It was found that essentially all of the virus activity present could be isolated in the form of crystalline material. The virus activity of this material was about five hundred times that of the starting material."

The Stanley findings illustrated that if viruses are *not* living in the strict sense of the word, they are perched somewhere on the threshold of life. Viruses, including the tobacco mosaic, are the ultimate parasites; they cannot reproduce unless they have another living cell to supply the ingredients for their own "life" processes. Yet when tobacco mosaic crystals are dissolved in water and injected into a tobacco plant, they multiply amazingly, increasing their number manyfold in a very short time.

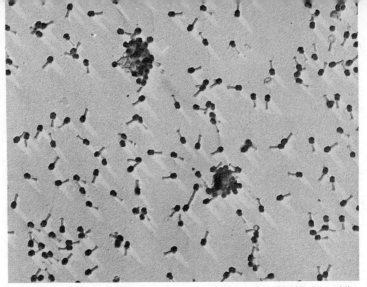

Fig. 33 An electrophotomicrograph at a magnification of 33,000 of paddle-shaped viruses known as bacteriophage $T_2$. Originally appeared in Journal of General Physiology, 40, 809, (57), reprinted here by permission Dr. R. M. Herriott, Johns Hopkins University School of Hygiene and Public Health, and Rockefeller University Press

In the twenty years that followed Dr. Stanley's purification and crystallization of the tobacco mosaic virus, many other viruses have received the same treatment. Meanwhile, the Nobel Prize winner became director of the University of California's Virus Laboratory in Berkeley, where in 1955 the virus that causes human polio was crystallized. Since then, several other human and animal viruses have been crystallized and carefully investigated under the eye of the electron microscope.

Viruses come in many shapes and sizes. They may be spherical, octagonal, or as with the tobacco mosaic virus, rod-shaped. The virus that infects the bacterium *E. coli* resembles a tiny canoe paddle.

Although their shapes vary, viruses are chemically very much alike. The virus "venom" is invariably a nucleic acid, either deoxyribosenucleic acid (DNA) or ribosenucleic acid (RNA). RNA occurs in most plant and animal viruses, whereas bacterial viruses, such as the one illustrated above, contain DNA.

Surrounding the nucleic acid core is a protective protein overcoat, the composition of which is determined by the nucleic acid it contains. Also within the nucleic acid is the genetic memory of the virus which makes its own reproduction possible.

When a virus works its way through the wall of a cell into its protoplasmic innards, it takes over the victim's biochemical machinery and greedily instructs the cell to make more nucleic acid for its growth and reproduction. In the process it deprives the cell of its own nucleic acid, reproduces at a fantastic rate, and leaves the cell along with its thousands of "brother and sister" viruses. Each new virus can then make its own deadly entry into another cell with the same disastrous results.

The symptoms of viral infections vary from sniffles and a cottony head through influenza, measles, mumps, chicken pox, yellow fever, polio, rabies and the wild undisciplined cell growth known as cancer. While it has been shown that viruses undoubtedly cause cancer in mice, rats, dogs, hamsters, chickens and other animals, the possibility that they cause human cancer is still based on circumstantial evidence. Under an electron microscope, virus particles have been seen in the blood of leukemia patients, but there is no proof that they are not relatively harmless viruses that just happen to be in the diseased cells. On that point, some researchers suspect that most of us may carry cancer viruses around with us to a greater or lesser extent, but they do not become dangerous until triggered by some insidious stimulus, such as atomic radiation or certain chemicals.

Dr. Ludwik Gross of the Veterans Administration Hospital, Bronx, New York, has treated perfectly normal mice with radiation, after which they soon developed cancer. In the cancer cells he found virus particles, which he passed on to other mice, and they also developed the disease. Many other experimental proofs and hypotheses have been proposed as backing for the virus-cancer link in humans but all the evidence is certainly not yet in.

In spite of the uncertainties, researchers are gaining the kind of experience that might help solve the human cancer problem if a virus is truly implicated. With what is now known about other virus diseases, it may be possible to develop an anticancer vaccine similar to those now used successfully against polio, the measles, smallpox and several varieties of influenza viruses. Or perhaps the search for antiviral drugs—this chapter's chief concern—may one day put an end to the cancer virus or viruses.

Until a few years ago, pharmaceutical researchers were not sure that they would ever be able to develop a really useful drug for any virus disease. Although viruses are relatively simple substances—a mixture of proteins and nucleic acids—researchers probably could not attack them at those biological points. The obstacle that looked so imposing at the time was the fact that living cells also depend on proteins and nucleic acids for survival; therefore, any drug aimed at either of the two viral constituents would almost certainly destroy useful cells in the process. To use such drugs as cures, says the German virologist Wolfhard Weidel, would be "like casting out the Devil with Beelzebub."

### IDU AND BLINDNESS

In attempting to thwart the virus at its own game, chemists have been relying heavily on the so-called antimetabolite approach. In this case, the drug is a substance which chokes off virus reproduction by inserting itself into the chemical machinery of the virus, particularly the nucleic acid portion.

One strategy is to stop the virus from scavenging the vital building blocks from the infecting cells by introducing another material that the virus uses instead. Rather than taking up the cell components that it ordinarily feeds on, the virus takes up the chemical interloper. The result is a new kind of virus particle, a virus particle that is biologically dead. Strangled with a metabolic clinker, it can no longer infect other cells or produce progeny.

Since 1961, researchers have become so enthusiastic about a virus-killer called 5-iododeoxyuridine, or IDU, that they do not feel as negative about the antiviral drug situation as they previously did. First synthesized by Dr. W. H. Prusoff of Yale University, IDU is now used very successfully in a localized eye infection that can cause blindness. Confronted with the biochemical fooler, the virus takes up the IDU molecules instead of thymidine, a cell ingredient that it requires for growth.

The *herpes simplex* virus, which also causes cold sores and fever blisters, sometimes attacks the cornea of the eye—the transparent part of the eyeball covering the iris and pupil. Dr. Herbert E. Kaufmann of the University of Florida College of Medicine was the first to use IDU to treat the virus disease—called *herpes keratitis*—in human eyes. The drug is applied very carefully to the infected area in a diluted solution or ointment and appears to block virus multiplication without irritation or damage to the uninfected eye tissue.

Since IDU first appeared, some ophthalmologists concede that it is a good, but not perfect, answer to *herpes keratitis.* Dr. Irving H. Leopold of Mount Sinai Hospital in New York warns that the drug does not perform well if the infection has worked deep into the cornea. More serious in the long run, says Dr. Leopold, is that some strains of the virus are becoming resistant to IDU. When resistance occurs, the alternatives are to use more of the same drug or shift to another one. The "use more" approach is ultimately self-defeating because there are always some viruses able to survive even large doses of the drug; and when they proceed to multiply and infect other cells, the original drug is essentially useless.

Following the same philosophy, virus researchers have come up with some new possibilities that might fill the gap if the resistance problem ever becomes too big for IDU to handle. At the Upjohn Company in Kalamazoo, Michigan, chemist James Hunter has synthesized an antiviral drug that appears to cure herpes infections in animal corneas that resist treatment with IDU. The new drug, called 1-beta-D-arabinofuranosyl cytosine, is also known as cytarabine or even more conveniently as CA. Whether it, too, will succumb to the resistance problem must await clinical testing and more widespread use.


### METHISAZONE AND SMALLPOX

In the United States, you have about a one-in-a-million chance of getting smallpox. Most American doctors have never even seen a smallpox patient. The incidence of this virus-caused disease is fortunately low because of compulsory vaccination programs and strict public health control at ports of entry. Yet in Asia and the Near East, smallpox is still a major scourge, compounded by a population explosion which puts more people closer together than they have ever been. In India alone, there are at least 300,000 cases of smallpox annually and those are only *reported* cases. Of the total number of cases, the death rate is about 30 percent, or about 100,000 men, women and children.

The smallpox statistics dramatize the fact that the disease is a part of the way of life in some areas, and that it is still uncontrolled in spite of the fact that usable vaccines are available. The reason the vaccine is not doing the job it might in the smallpox-saturated areas is that it is often very difficult to get it to people in time to protect them.

Because smallpox is transmitted by a virus, drug researchers have not been too encouraged about the possibility of a chemical agent that might cure it. As you read earlier, a drug attack on the protein or nucleic acid section of the virus might also damage the essential cells, and since smallpox can spread through the body, prospects for drug treatment looked even more bleak. Then came the thiosemicarbazones.

Since 1950, researchers have known that drugs of the thiosemicarbazone family would protect animals from experimentally induced "vaccinia" infections. Other laboratory tests indicated that some of the drugs were active against a range of virus diseases, including rabies and *herpes simplex*.

Clinically, the drugs lay dormant until 1963, when one of the most active members of the series—called methisazone—was put into large-scale field trials in areas where smallpox abounds. Under the direction of Dr. D. John Bauer of the Wellcome Laboratories of Tropical Medicine in London, England, the new drug was given to 2,300 people in Madras in the middle of a larger than usual smallpox epidemic. The people who took the drug, in a vanilla-flavored preparation, were close relatives of patients who had already been infected with smallpox. Because they lived so close to the pox-afflicted individuals, the chances of their getting the disease were only too good. Of the 2,300 people who took the drug, says Dr. Bauer, 6 got smallpox. According to the normal disease rate in the area, between 100 to 120 would have contracted the disease.

Drug researchers from various laboratories believe that when a virus enters a cell containing methisazone, the drug seems to prevent the virus from putting its two essential components together; i.e., the protein and nucleic acid. The infected cell dies, but the virus can go no further. "The virus particle virtually falls into a death trap from which it cannot escape," says Dr. Bauer.

In practice, methisazone is given before a person becomes ill with smallpox, so that the drug can kill the virus before it can enter too many cells. Dr. Bauer suspects that methisazone or a drug like it, if used properly, could potentially wipe out smallpox in areas where it is now such a deadly accessory to life.

"Theorizing, one can say that if in these countries every single person was given a dose of the drug tomorrow, and perhaps a mopping-up operation was carried out a month later, smallpox would be exterminated," says Dr. Bauer.

In addition to the successful smallpox trials in Madras, methisazone has also been tested in Brazil against alastrim, a milder form of smallpox. Here too, protection was high, according to the Brazilian researchers. Other studies show that the drug helps victims of *vaccinia gangrenosa,* an invariably deadly infection caused by vaccinations that do not heal properly.

## NATURAL ANTIVIRAL MATERIALS

All of the drugs mentioned previously came about through the careful laboratory manipulations of chemists, but nature is also getting into the antiviral act.

Extracts of the lemon balm plant (*Melissa officinalis*), known to witch doctors and medical folk lorists for centuries, were very effective against *herpes simplex* virus in chick embryonated eggs, according to Dr. L. S. Kucera of the Mayo Clinic.

Clams and other shellfish contain substances—called paolins—that can delay the onset of virus-caused tumors in hamsters, report researchers of the National Institutes of Health in Bethesda, Maryland. The virus that induced the tumors, incidentally, was an adenovirus of the type that causes respiratory infections in human beings. An extract of seaweed, or kelp, which appears to contain both carbohydrates and protein, suppressed influenza viruses in chicken eggs, according to Dr. R. H. Kathan of the University of Illinois Medical School.

In late 1965, the University of Florida's Dr. Ysolina Centifanto, working in Dr. Kaufman's laboratory, discovered that an extract of certain bacteria which had been infected with a bacterial virus, or phage, is a very potent antiviral substance. The material—called Phagicin —partially identified as a polypeptide, can cure *herpes keratitis* in laboratory animals and appears harmless to normal cells, says Dr. Kaufman. In test-tube experiments it also appears effective against vaccinia and other viruses that affect man.

Antibiotics, such as the tetracyclines and penicillin, are probably the best known naturally produced drugs, but until recently pharmaceutical chemists have not been able to develop any with antiviral activity. This did not surprise them too much, because antibiotics usually work against biochemical soft spots (such as cell walls in bacteria) that the less sophisticated viruses do not have.

One new antibiotic, from a harmless soil bacterium —*Streptomyces hygroscopis*—inhibited influenza and polio viruses in mice, according to Dr. D. C. DeLong and his fellow scientists at Eli Lilly and Company in Indianapolis. This compound has the distinction of working in animals, while being completely inactive in preliminary test-tube trials. To Dr. DeLong this suggests that drug researchers should not give up too quickly if cell culture tests do not produce quick results.

Another antiviral antibiotic was discovered by accident in Iran in a test tube containing human cells infected with the Sindbis virus. Because the virus did not damage the cells as expected, Dr. Kiarash Naficy of the University of Teheran looked more closely and noticed a mold growing in the test tube. Cultivation of the mold in the appropriate medium grew enough of the material so that it could be identified as *Penicillium cyclopium,* a relative of the great-granddaddy of all antibiotics, penicillin. In mice it interfered with the progress of adenovirus and the West Nile virus.

### THE UNIVERSAL VIRUS KILLER

Only two years after Wendell Stanley crystallized the tobacco mosaic virus, two British researchers, F. O. MacCallum and G. W. M. Findlay, made what could be one of the most significant observations ever to occur in the virus field. They noticed that monkeys afflicted with a virus infection known as Rift Valley fever were relatively immune to the virus that causes yellow fever. Healthy monkeys were not. On the surface, the explanation seemed obvious. Antibodies produced in response to the Rift Valley fever were also able to suppress the yellow fever virus. Though it may have seemed logical at the time, Findlay and MacCallum learned that the suggested answer was the wrong one. When they treated healthy monkeys with antibodies from monkeys infected with Rift Valley fever, and then exposed the healthy monkeys to yellow fever, they were not protected from the latter disease. Findlay and MacCallum then wondered, "If it was not the antibodies that protected the monkeys, what was it?"

Following up their earlier observations, the British team discovered that a similar situation occurred in laboratory cultures of living animal cells. If they were infected with one virus, they seemed to resist the encroachments of a second virus, as if something in the cell was providing interference against the new virus invader.

Now, evidence is beginning to accumulate that human beings may also have the machinery for creating the same type of viral interference noted in cell cultures and animals. In recent trials of the polio vaccine in Mexico, many children were resistant to the vaccine, which contained "live" but weakened polio virus. At the same time, the children suffered from a virus-caused intestinal infection which holds forth in areas where health and sanitation facilities are not the best. Somehow the intestinal virus seemed to be blunting the effects of the active virus portion of the polio vaccine. This deduction is strengthened by the coincidental fact that polio epidemics are rare where the intestinal virus runs rampant.

In 1957, another insight into the unknown factor that

blocked virus infections was revealed in England, where in fact it was first observed twenty years earlier. Drs. Alick Isaacs and Jean Lindenmann of the National Institute for Medical Research in London were experimenting with an influenza virus that had been killed with heat. When the virus was added to a cell culture and then combined with other cells, the new batch of cells was able to resist attack by a second virus. When they tried another virus, the cells were still resistant. With another the results were the same. Something in the culture was making the cells immune to almost any virus they encountered.

Shortly after, the British group isolated a substance in the infected cell line that was not found in normal cells. It was a protein and they called it interferon.

More discoveries followed. Interferon was produced in all species of animals studied by the London research team, and in all instances, a given interferon protected against many virus types. Visions of a universal virus cure were obscured temporarily when the scientists found that interferon from one species *would not* work in another. Chick interferon would not protect a mouse against virus infection, and vice versa. Hopes revived when Dr. Isaacs and his co-workers discovered that in one important case, interferon broke the species barrier. Interferon produced in monkey cells was also active in infected human cells in the test tube.

Knowing what interferon was told little about how it worked. Its performance was full of immunological contradictions. It was a protein, all right, and antibodies are also proteins. Immunologists know that when the body produces antibodies against a disease, they usually act only against that disease agent. Interferon, on the other hand, appeared to take on all the viruses it ran against.

Then the English researchers took a new tack. Perhaps a cell produced interferon in response to the *nucleic acid* portion of the virus. It was realized by then that it was the nucleic acid of a virus that did the actual infecting when it entered a cell.

In a follow-up experiment, Dr. Isaacs and his colleagues treated *mouse* cells with RNA from a culture of *chick* cells. RNA, or ribosenucleic acid, is responsible for protein production in all living cells, and is the infecting end of certain viruses. Once the *mouse* cells were fed the *chick* RNA, they reacted as if it were a foreign virus; interferon was produced, which in turn protected the cells against infection by complete viruses. On the heels of that lead, Dr. Isaacs added mouse RNA to another culture of mouse cells. This time, no interferon was produced, and important answers were emerging.

When the cell produced interferon, Dr. Isaacs proposed, it was reacting to a foreign strain of nucleic acid. When it met nucleic acid from its own species, nothing happened. Another experiment showed that if the RNA were chemically altered, then added to another culture of chick cells, the cells again responded as if it were foreign, and made interferon.

In 1964, Dr. Alvin Glasky and Dr. Jacob C. Holper of Abbott Laboratories in Chicago made more biochemical sense out of the previously confusing interferon situation. Reporting to the Sixth International Congress of Biochemistry in New York, Dr. Glasky said that interferon seems to hit an invading virus at one of its most important biochemical production lines. He noted that when the virus breaks through the wall of a hapless cell, it induces the formation of an enzyme which it uses to build up new DNA or RNA molecules from materials that it steals from the infected cell. In DNA viruses, the enzyme is called DNA synthetase; in an RNA virus, the enzyme is RNA synthetase.

Interferon seems to block these enzymes before they can make a single new virus particle, the Abbott researchers found, and again their experiments point up how selective interferon is. For instance, the enzyme from calf cells infected with influenza virus is inhibited by calf interferon but is untouched by the interferon from infected chick or rabbit cells.

To recapitulate what thirty years of research have revealed about interferon:

1. Interferon is a protein produced in a cell after it has been infected by a virus.

2. Interferon is species specific; that is, if it will protect a chicken against new virus invaders, the same interferon will not work in a monkey.

3. When interferon is produced in a cell, it blocks the action of an enzyme which normally converts the constituents of an infected cell into new virus particles.

4. Because it is effective against so many viruses, it has been suggested as a powerful antiviral agent of possible therapeutic use in man.

On that last point, it is believed that interferon produced by our cells is already doing a very good job of protecting us against the many different viruses that we encounter every day. Much of this protection comes from the antibodies that our body produces against the protein overcoat of the virus, but they are obviously not the entire answer. Because patients who have a condition in which they cannot produce antibodies seem to be able to hold their own against viruses, Dr. Isaacs believes that their recovery from virus infections may be largely due to interferon.

## PRODUCTION PROBLEMS

Since about 1962, British pharmaceutical houses have been carrying out a government-backed project geared to determining whether or not interferon really is the wonder substance it appears to be. Because they had been very successful in developing production methods for polio virus vaccines, the government asked the drug houses to see what they could do about producing interferon.

The pharmaceutical houses were prodded by data that indicated some likely applications for interferon in human medicine. In a test carried out by the Medical Research Council, thirty-eight previously unvaccinated volunteers were injected with interferon and a neutral substance on different parts of the body. When the volunteers were then injected with smallpox vaccine containing the vaccinia virus, the vaccination "took" on the neutral skin areas in thirty-seven out of thirty-eight cases. However, in those areas where interferon had been injected, only fourteen vaccinations took. Apparently the interferon had made the other twenty-four volunteers resistant to the vaccinia virus.

In a related study, five patients suffering from eye infections caused by vaccinia virus were treated with interferon. Within twenty-four hours, most of their symptoms had disappeared.

As soon as the pharmaceutical manufacturers threw

themselves into the interferon problem, they ran up against several troubling obstacles. One of them was determining the exact chemical composition of interferon. Although all sources agreed that it was a protein, they dis-' agreed on the important matter of molecular weight, that is, its relative weight compared to an atom of hydrogen. Estimates of interferon's molecular weight varied between 15,000 to 80,000, which is a much wider quality control spread than drug producers like to work with. A more recent consensus supports a molecular weight of about 34,000.

British drug researchers also found that separation of the interferon from the hundreds of other substances that surround it was especially frustrating. One firm reported that it was able to get only about a millionth of a gram of interferon from a little more than a quart of tissue culture fluid.

Although some American researchers report finding interferon in human blood, it is unlikely that human cells would ever be the production source of the antiviral substance. There is the double difficulty of getting enough living human tissue to work with and then developing culture methods for production of the antiviral substance. Because monkey interferon combats human viruses in a cell culture, it is possible that monkey cells might be used to make the substance commercially; but this also hinges on whether or not purification methods can be developed.

Some biochemists suggest that they may someday be able to make synthetic versions of interferon for medical use, just as they have with many other naturally occurring drugs. Another possibility now under consideration is to develop some way of inducing the cell to produce extra supplies of interferon to ward off future virus attacks. For example, Dr. T. C. Merigan and his group at the Stanford University School of Medicine note that Statolon, a polymeric sugar produced by a mold, induces interferon production both in animals and cell cultures. Others suggest inoculating the individual with harmless viruses, or perhaps even a foreign strain of nucleic acid to promote interferon production.

### THE VIRUS-CANCER LINK

Earlier you read that the link between viruses and human cancer has never been completely forged. However, it is known that a number of hydrocarbons definitely cause cancer in man. Scientists believe that these "carcinogenic hydrocarbons" are able to spur latent or "hidden" cancer viruses into action, but no one has been able to say why this happens. Recent work in Belgium suggests that interferon is a biochemical middleman between carcinogens and cancer-causing viruses. Dr. Edward De Maeyer and his wife, Jacqueline De Maeyer-Guignard, found that well-known carcinogenic hydrocarbons inhibit interferon production in rat tumor cells infected with virus. As a result, the virus grows as if the interferon were not present.

Extrapolating the Belgian experiments, it is possible to theorize that cancer-causing viruses are held in control by interferon until a carcinogenic hydrocarbon enters the cell. The hydrocarbon then ties up the interferon, and the virus is free to reproduce, with all biochemical inhibitions released.

# CHAPTER 11

## BATTLE ON
## THE BUG FRONT

This chapter is *not* an apologia for the use of chemical insecticides, even though they make an excellent case for themselves in a dispassionate discussion. Farmers like these man-made bug-killers that have emerged since World War II; they act quickly, sometimes controlling an insect infestation overnight; they raise crop yields; they put more money in the pocketbook. But not only farmers are grateful. The use of DDT in malaria zones has saved millions of lives by eradicating the anopheles mosquito.

Nevertheless, poorly planned, often irresponsible use of insecticides has aroused fears among conservationists that the chemical agents may be a little too efficient. Along with the suppression of the boll weevil, the gypsy moth, the Japanese beetle and hundreds of other crop pests, insecticides have also taken a toll among beneficial insects, domestic animals, wild game, fish, birds—and even man. Residues of certain insecticides seem to be accumulating in soil, water, crops, animals and man. Most frustrating of all is the observation that insects are becoming resistant to the effects of insecticides almost as fast as chemists invent new ones.

Do the positive accomplishments of chemical insecticides balance the potential and real hazards that accompany their careless use? There is no easy answer to that question. Farmers are satisfied that insecticides increase their chances of success in an area that is always a constant struggle with nature. Conservationists rightfully lament the death of a robin and the spectre of a silent spring. Some biologists who believe that nature holds the key to its own survival protest that "the ecological balance" is tilting dangerously against man's own welfare. Some critics point out that there are many other ways of controlling harmful insects, and that scientists should be working in these new unexplored directions.

The real purpose of this chapter is to demonstrate that scientists have not been asleep all these years: entomologists, zoologists, plant pathologists and chemists have been aware of those "new unexplored directions" in agricultural research for several decades, and they are not placing all their bets on bigger and better insecticides.

### INSECT CONTROL WITH INSECT DISEASES

It may sound like an agricultural researcher's pipe dream, but scientists have recently become very enthusiastic about a number of "insecticides" that have the following high-powered qualifications:

1. They are completely harmless to men, animals and beneficial insects.
2. Extremely small amounts—often less than an ounce —will treat a ten-acre plot.

3. Once they take hold, these insecticides are able to reproduce and go on to attack other insects in the area.

The new excitement in the laboratory and the field springs from recent developments in the insect pathogen area where it is now known that more than 1,200 viruses, fungi, protozoa and other disease agents can wreak disaster on insect populations. Scientists have successfully isolated many of these agents and are now creating man-made epidemics to wipe out several costly crop pests.

As early as 1891, researchers were grinding up virus-diseased insects and applying them to infested areas to control insects of the same type. Since then scientists have learned how to use the purified viruses themselves to get even better results on a much larger scale.

"In my opinion, viruses have the greatest potential for use in this new kind of insect control," says Dr. A. M. Heimpel, senior insect pathologist at the USDA Beltsville labs.

"Viruses are very highly specific, they act in a matter of days before heavy crop damage is done. After the insect dies, he deposits a new load of virus on the plant, and other insects then become infected."

Dr. Heimpel and his colleagues all over the world have identified more than 250 species of insect viruses, each of which infects only that species. Of the viruses, less than 10 percent have been used in insect-control field trials, some with great success.

The fact that insect viruses are already found in nature is an outstanding recommendation for their use, says Dr. Heimpel. Anyone who has ever eaten raw cabbage has probably taken in a small amount of the virus that is death to the cabbage looper. This is an insect that cuts large gouges out of cabbage leaves, as the name suggests. The virus is also found in the soil wherever the cabbage is growing, posing no hazard, as far as is now known, to any other insect, plant or animal.

Viruses of the so-called polyhedral type have already been used effectively against the cabbage looper, cotton bollworm and the tobacco budworm. These last two insects rank next to the boll weevil as cotton destroyers.

Polyhedral viruses get their names from their characteristic many-sided shape. Chemically they are like most other viruses, consisting of a rod-shaped infective core of nucleic acid surrounded by a tough protein overcoat that protects it from the elements. Also like other viruses, they occupy a strange half-world between the living and non-living. Viruses are the ultimate parasite; they can reproduce only by entering the cells of some other living organism, whereupon they take over the cell's reproductive machinery, manufacturing millions of other brother viruses at the expense of the infected cell.

Mr. C. M. Ignoffo, formerly of the USDA and now with the Bioferm Division of International Minerals and Chemical Corporation, recently perfected a mass-production technique for the nuclear polyhedral virus of the cotton bollworm that makes its use in the field a distinct possibility.

The first step in the mass production of the virus is to place the insect larva in a plastic cup where it can feed happily on a specially prepared diet. The larvae are strongly cannibalistic, and if they were not kept apart, they would eat each other, says Mr. Ignoffo.

The well-fed larvae are then sprayed with a small amount of polyhedral virus, and in a short time the cells of the insect are literally exploding with virus particles. Within a few days one larva will manufacture as many as two trillion polyhedral viruses. One hundred boll-worms produce enough viruses to treat an acre of plants.

Although insect viruses are not yet commercially available, other types of microbial control have a pretty good field record. Take *Baccillus thuringiensis,* for example.

More than fifty years ago, scientists isolated that bacterial substance from diseased larvae of the Mediterranean flour moth. Today, spores of these bacteria—or their close relatives—are being used to combat more than a hundred different types of destructive larvae from the *Lepidoptera* group, which includes moths and butterflies.

In the United States, the pioneering work on *Bacillus thuringiensis* must be credited to Dr. E. A. Steinhaus, head of the Division of Biological Sciences at the University of California at Irvine. Dr. Steinhaus, a true innovator in the use of insect diseases as pest control agents, first reported that the bacteria could destroy the alfalfa caterpillar. Since then, he and other researchers have been adding almost an insect a month to the bacteria-susceptible list.

The powerful punch of *Bacillus thuringiensis* comes from a diamond-shaped crystal produced by bacterial spores which act by paralyzing the insect's digestive tract. Researchers have recently found that the bacteria produce at least five different toxic substances, one of which acts by paralyzing the insect's digestive tract.

Now used to control a wide range of pests on corn, lettuce, cauliflower, cabbage and other cole crops, the material is now produced commercially by fermentation in huge 10,000-gallon vats. This is the same technique used to manufacture many of today's most powerful antibiotics, as well as beer, a product of less well-defined medical value.

The Bioferm Division of the International Mineral and Chemical Corp. in Wasco, California, developed the first really successful mass production technique for *Bacillus thuringiensis*, and this "living insecticide" is now being manufactured in France, Germany, Czechoslovakia and Russia.

A suburbanite who has seen his rosebushes, prize evergreens and trees swarming with Japanese beetles should be comforted by the knowledge that the shiny green insect is only a minor, relatively short-term problem. Past experience indicates that inevitably the beetle grubs, which can quickly convert a lush lawn into an unappealing stubble, will be eliminated by a bacterial disease distributed in the soil by the insect itself.

Spores of the disease—called *B. popilliae,* or milky disease—will control most of the beetle grubs in a season or two. If the lawnowner does not want to wait for nature to take its course, he can hurry it along with a powdered form of the disease, now available at garden supply stores. The spore powder will usually decimate the grub population in a matter of two months. As he applies the powder to his lawn, the suburbanite might take a moment or two to think kindly of Dr. S. R. Dutky, the USDA researcher who first made the spore powder available for public use.

### ATTRACTIVE APPROACHES TO INSECT CONTROL

To accentuate the positive side of chemical insecticides, and minimize the potential hazards, agricultural researchers are eagerly searching for refined methods of application that will be called up only when needed, where needed and with a wide safety margin for beneficial insects, birds, wild game, domestic animals and man. Ideally they would like to be able to detect a harmful insect invasion as soon as it occurs, then use the minimum amount of insecticide to treat the affected areas. One approach to more prudent use of chemical bug-killers has proved itself over and over again: it is the use of attractants to lure insects into traps where they can be counted and perhaps destroyed.

The first large-scale use of man-made insect attractants was made in response to the periodic appearances of the Mediterranean fruit fly (medfly) in Florida. When the medfly becomes entrenched in a fruit orchard, its larval stage can spoil crops and cut profits in a matter of days. In 1956, the United States Department of Agriculture confronted a medfly invasion head on and spent eleven million dollars to wipe out the pest. The successful crash program—using conventional methods—took about a year, but its success did not put an end to the threat of other medfly invasions that could happen any time.

To nip other medfly invasions in the bud, USDA chemists set out to develop chemical agents that could sniff out medflies (or perhaps it is the other way around) as soon as they arrive. Part of this program involved testing thousands of different compounds from laboratories all over the country with a simple device called an olfactometer. Glass traps containing the candidate attractants were hung in a screened eight-foot enclosure. Depending on the number of medflies that congregated in the different traps, the attractant that lured the most flies got the highest rating.

When a good lead turns up, the USDA chemists test

chemical relatives of the likely attractant, if they are available. If they are not, they build their own chemical changes into the original molecule, tacking on an atomic grouping here, removing another atomic grouping elsewhere to see if it improves in attractancy. The most active attractants are retested in the laboratory, and if they fare well there, they are sent out into the field to see how they perform under natural conditions.

This kind of chemical hunt can be stimulating, frustrating or both. For example, the first promising medfly attractant synthesized by USDA research chemists under Dr. Morton Beroza in Beltsville did very well in the laboratory and the field. It was called Siglure. (One of its close relatives performed even better in the laboratory tests, but when it was subjected to the heat, humidity, wind, rain and other complications of outdoor life it failed miserably.) But even Siglure was not perfect, or so it seemed.

Some batches of the chemical were excellent medfly attractants, others were unexpectedly poor. Stymied by the anomalous results, the USDA chemists exposed the questionable batches to further scrutiny and found that they contained different types of Siglure molecules. Both molecules contained the same atoms of carbon, hydrogen and oxygen in the same concentration, but they were not really identical, but only so-called spatial isomers (equal in parts). In what chemists call the *cis* isomer, the two groups indicated were on the same side of the six-sided benzene ring. In the *trans* isomer, they were diagonally opposite each other. This subtle difference in spatial arrangement of the constituent atoms was enough to make the medfly flock to the *trans* form and ignore the *cis* isomer.

As attractive as the *trans* form was, the USDA chemists

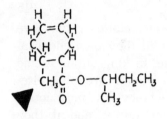

Cis-Siglure           Trans-Siglure

# SIGLURE

Fig. 34

beefed up its power significantly by treating it with hydrogen chloride. The resulting compound—called trimedlure—is the most powerful medfly lure ever developed.

Since trimedlure was synthesized by Dr. Beroza in 1959, it has been used to detect several other incipient medfly buildups before they could really take hold. Usually these fruit fly incursions have been wiped out one or two months after detection, saving the government millions of dollars in potential eradication costs.

One of the most successful trials of insect attractants took place on the Pacific isle of Rota, where USDA scientists used a man-made material called methyleugenol to lure the oriental fruit fly to an insecticide, and within five months the species disappeared from the island. Though the insecticide did the killing, the male fruit fly likes the attractant so much that if there is enough around it will gorge itself to death.

Another man-made lure called "cue-lure" or 4-p-acetoxyphenyl-2-butanone has been used in USDA find-and-destroy programs in Hawaii. In spite of its name, the melon fly is not that selective in its appetite, attacking

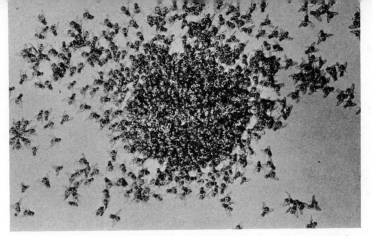

Fig. 35 A few drops of methyleugenol will bring thousands of oriental fruit flies from all directions. *United States Department of Agriculture*

eighty different plant species, including the tomato and cucumber. In the Hawaii test, cue-lure did its job well, attracting only male melon flies and none of the hundreds of other insects that inhabit our fiftieth state.

The European chafer, an insect that infests pastures, grain crops and turf in the northeastern United States, is strongly drawn to a synthetic material named butyl sorbate. This too, is being used in USDA-sponsored chafer control programs.

No one knows why trimedlure or the other man-made attractants make insects wing their way to traps set up in the field or harbor areas where they most often appear. The materials do not exist in nature, and they do not seem to be related to natural substances known to attract insects to their food, egg-laying sites or nests.

Scientists have long been convinced that if they could harness whatever it is that draws a male insect to the female or vice versa, they would have an attractant that would be hard to beat. Since the end of the nineteenth century, researchers have been aware that the female gypsy moth emits a fantastically powerful perfume that can entice male moths a mile away. The gypsy moth, accidentally introduced into Massachusetts from France in 1869, has played havoc with American forests ever since, and it has always been high on the government's "must go" list.

For many years, a crude extract of the abdominal segments of the female moth has been used as a probe for infestations of the multi-million-dollar forest pest, but the primitive technique left much to be desired. Collecting the moths, sometimes from as far away as Europe, was extremely costly and time-consuming. A man-made version of the moth's love lure seemed to be a much more practical and scientific answer to the problem.

Just about the time Dr. Beroza put the finishing touches on the trimedlure work, another USDA chemist named Martin Jacobson set out to isolate, identify and perhaps prepare a laboratory version of whatever it was that made the female gypsy moth so attractive to the male. The first step was getting enough gypsy moths, and this was no easy task.

In the early summer, field men from the Plant Pest Control Division would go out and collect the pupae of the female moths, which are about twice the size of the males. Pupae are the dormant stage of some insect life cycles between the larval and moth phases. After the moths emerged, the field men removed the last two abdominal segments of the females, dropped them in benzene solvent and sent them to Beltsville laboratories. Then it was up to Mr. Jacobson to extract the moth lure.

A half-million moths and a year later—in 1960—the Beltsville group was able to isolate two small drops of pure attractant from all those abdominal segments. Even that small amount was enough for Mr. Jacobson and his associates to show that the enticing moth perfume was

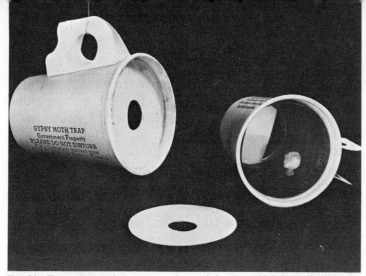

Fig. 36 The gypsy moth trap currently used by the USDA is made from an inexpensive paper cup. The moth, lured to the attractant on the small cotton ball, enters the trap and becomes stuck to the adhesive lining the cup. *United States Department of Agriculture*

a material with the unromantic name of 10-acetoxy-*cis*-7-hexadecen-1-ol.

In laboratory tests, a millionth of a millionth of a millionth of a gram of the pure lure could make the male moth more than a little excited; in the field, the males flew in from all directions. Soon after, the USDA chemists were able to synthesize the gypsy moth lure in the laboratory in a ten-step process, complicated enough to make its bulk production very unlikely. Fortunately a close relative of the lure, with just about the same attractiveness, could be made in two steps starting with a castor oil ingredient, probably not too attractive to anyone.

The synthetic moth lure—dubbed gyplure—is now used in thousands of paper cup traps hung in the forests of the Northeastern United States. Male moths that fly to the traps, expecting to meet their mates, find only a sticky substance called Tanglefoot, which keeps them there until the mothcounters come. The USDA researchers hope that this kind of survey program, in combination with conventional bug killers or newly developing eradication methods will eventually help eliminate the gypsy moth from that part of the country.

In passing, it should be mentioned that gyplure will probably never be a big seller for agricultural chemical manufacturers—"The synthetic attractant is so powerful a lure for the male that one pound of the material—which could sell for less than ten dollars a pound—will be sufficient for all the plant control needs in the gypsy moth survey program for the *next three hundred years*," says Mr. Jacobson.

In addition to the lure of the female gypsy moth, sex attractants have also been found in some species of butterflies, wasps, bees, ants, beetles, flies, mosquitoes, termites, grasshoppers and cockroaches. Very few of these have yet been chemically identified and synthesized as was the case with the gypsy moth lure.

Of all the attractants, there are probably few more powerful than that of the American cockroach. The female of the species of the familiar household pest produces such an exotic aroma that one/one-hundred-quintillionth of a gram will make the male sit up and take notice. The roach lure was first isolated by Dr. Denis R. A. Wharton and his associates at the United States Army Natick Laboratories in Massachusetts. Dr. Wharton found that if a female cockroach merely passed over a piece of porous paper, the paper was almost as exciting to the male cockroach as the female itself.

Still another insect *femme fatale* is the virgin female pine sawfly. When University of Wisconsin researchers hung a cage containing this attractive female in the middle of the forest, she enticed 7,000 males between 11

A.M. and 4 P.M. Each day after that she attracted about 1,000 males, whereupon she died on the fifth day. Even in death, what was left of her lure was sufficient to attract a few interested male stragglers.

The sex attractant of the pink bollworm moth—one of the most destructive of all American crop pests—was also identified and isolated by USDA researchers. A crude extractant has already been used successfully to survey concentrations of the pest in the cotton-growing areas of Texas, Arizona and New Mexico.

In Germany, researchers isolated the sex attractant of the female domestic silkworm moth. They called the material "bombykol." Its chemical name is a tongue twister: *trans*-10-*cis*-12-hexadecadien-1-ol.

The molecular structure of bombykol is similar to the lure of the gypsy moth; in fact, Mr. Jacobson reports that the attractant of the queen bee for the drone, and the lures of the Indian water bug and the bronze orange bug all show striking chemical resemblances.

### THWARTING THE SEX URGE

While one school of agricultural researchers is trying to lure male insects to their doom with chemical promises of female companionship, another school is taking advantage of the same urge in a different way.

The philosophy of this promising new approach is to fill infested areas with male insects which cannot successfully fertilize the female. These insects—sterilized by atomic radiation or chemicals—would overwhelm the female population by sheer force of numbers, but when they mated, no progeny would result. This idea, a long-time predilection of the USDA's Dr. E. F. Knipling, would, it is hoped, eliminate all of certain unwanted insects in a short time, at low cost, with no hazard to other living things.

The first insect to be attacked by the sterilization technique was the screwworm fly, which lays its eggs in the wounds of warm-blooded animals, especially cattle, other livestock and wildlife. When the eggs hatch, the parasitic larvae feed on the animal's flesh, sometimes killing the animal in as little as ten days.

In a preliminary field test in 1954, thousands of male screwworm flies were reared and irradiated with gamma rays in "screwworm factories." The sterile males were then released on the 170-square-mile island of Curacao in the Dutch West Indies in such numbers that they cornered most of the available female screwworm fly market. In the meanwhile normal males in the native population had little opportunity to compete with their foreign brothers. As for the females, they mated with the more readily available sterile males and died without having produced any larvae. The end result was that this important livestock cattle parasite quickly disappeared from the island.

In 1958, the sterile fly technique was moved closer to home; to Florida and the Southeastern United States where the screwworm was a major pest. The USDA airdropped three and a quarter billion radiation-sterilized flies in several waves over an area of 85,000 miles. Seventeen months later, there was not a single screwworm to be found, chalking up a victory that now saves cattle raisers an estimated twenty million dollars in yearly losses.

In 1963, the USDA's Agricultural Research Service used the same radiation sterilization technique to wipe out the oriental fruit fly population on the Pacific isle of Guam. The cost of this eradication program was about four cents an acre, considerably less than any other control program.

In another field trial, the radiation sterilization eliminated the melon fly from Rota, a Pacific isle about thirty-seven miles northeast of Guam. As in other experiments, both male and female flies were sterilized while still in the pupae state. Although the program was eventually successful, success did not come easily. The sterilized melon fly pupae were put in small ventilated boxes, and after emerging as flies, they were dropped from airplanes in a series of "bombing runs." However, the researchers did not take into account the fact that Rota's animal life might welcome the melon flies from heaven, and when the partially opened boxes landed, many of the sterile flies were devoured by toads, birds, poultry and lizards. Other birds invented a little game in which they would wait for the boxes to drop from the plane, then follow them to the ground, eating melon fly pupae all the way down.

Aside from the fact that the animal world was making great inroads into the success of the project, typhoons Karen and Olive blew across Rota at the time, picking up some unsterilized, fertile flies from nearby Guam. In spite of the many difficulties, the USDA researchers found that in the period from September, 1962, to December, 1963, the thriving melon fly population dropped from millions to zero.

The dramatic successes of the radiation sterilization program speaks for itself, but the method has a few admitted shortcomings. For instance, the rearing of billions of insects, sterilizing them and releasing them into infested areas is an enormously demanding task. Another

shortcoming of radiation treatment is that the sterile flies
are sometimes slightly less vigorous in the pursuit of the
female than their normal brothers are.

Within the last decade the USDA's Entomology Research Division has been carrying out an energetic program aimed at developing chemical sterilants that might
obviate some of the inherent disadvantages of the radiation method. Ideally, the chemical sterilants, if proved
safe, would be mixed with food baits or attractants.

Since 1958, the USDA has screened more than 2,500
different chemicals as potential sterilizing agents for
houseflies and other insects. Houseflies are used as a preliminary screen because they are easy to raise, breed fast
and produce quick results. From a more practical point
of view, they represent one of the most infamous disease
carriers in the insect world.

Until 1964, the most interesting chemosterilants came
from two general chemical classes, the antimetabolites
and the alkylating agents. An antimetabolite thwarts the
reproductive potential of an insect by interfering with
the ability of its cells to make substances that it needs for
growth and survival. Alkylating agents act very much like
radiation in that they damage the reproductive cells'
nucleic acids, the genetic materials without which an insect cannot reproduce. Because they inhibit cellular
growth so effectively, both types of compound have been
used widely in the treatment of human cancer.

Generally, the alkylating agents have outstripped the
antimetabolites as chemosterilants. Among the most
promising are "tepa," "metepa," "thiotepa" and "apholate." (Their much longer names would run several lines.)
These compounds may be lumped loosely into a chemical
group known as the aziridinyl phosphines.

Since 1964, another chemosterilant type, which steps

outside both of the above classifications, was developed in the laboratories of the USDA's Dr. Alexej Borkovec. These new materials—called dimethylamine derivatives—appear to have a much more selective action than the earlier compounds, which sterilize a wide range of insects. Hempa, one of the best of the new group, is particularly appealing because there is a 20-to-1 spread between the dose that will kill a fly and the dose that will sterilize it. This is important because obviously one sterilized fly can reduce the population to a much greater extent than a single dead fly. Backing up this point, laboratory tests showed that normal female houseflies produced only sterile eggs after mating with male flies that were fed on a diet containing 1 percent Hempa.

Field tests of the new chemosterilants have been limited, and they still cannot claim as massive a victory as the eradication of the screwworm fly with released radiation-sterilized males. Because so little is known of their toxicity to man and other mammals, most field tests have been carried out in restricted areas where populations of harmful insects are known to rest and breed.

For example, when tepa and apholate were sprayed over a refuse dump, swarming with flies, the population was drastically reduced, says Dr. Germain La Brecque of the USDA's Entomology Research Division in Gainesville, Florida. In another limited test, he found that if he placed liquid baits laced with metepa or Hempa in poultry houses the housefly population dropped to zero in a matter of weeks.

More recently, pupae of Mexican fruit flies were dipped in tepa and released along the border between California and Mexico. Because the flies usually do not stray far from the release area, they formed a sterilizing barrier against normal flies inclined to make the northward trip to the fruit and vegetable fields of California.

Chemosterilants may someday be used in a two-pronged exploitation of the relentless sex drive of target insects, says Dr. La Brecque. In the first phase, the insects would be lured to a trap containing a chemical attractant. Instead of a friendly female, the male would find only food; food impregnated with a chemosterilant. Disappointed, but happy with the free meal, the male would feed his frustrated self and wing off into the forest to find a female. Again, if the sterile male meets and mates with a normal female, the end result of his long search would be an additional drop in the fly population.

Because they *are* chemicals, the insect sterilants potentially carry any or all of the disadvantages ascribed to conventional bug-killers. The toxic effects of the new materials on man and animals have still not been completely explored, and there are already indications that insects can develop resistance to the sterilants. However, most scientists believe that because of the chemical composition of the chemosterilants, they are easily broken down in the soil, and will probably never add up to a serious insecticide residue problem. In addition, present plans call for a restricted, tightly controlled use of the sterilants; they will not be sprayed over hundreds of acres of crop or forest land. For this reason alone, health hazards should be kept to a comfortable minimum. Add to that the fact that chemists are convinced they can so refine the molecular structure of the chemosterilants that new and as yet unmade compounds will affect only a given class of insects and leave other species alone.

### THE REPELLENT APPROACH

Now that they can attract crop pests to a mate that is not there or to a mate that will never be able to add to the insect population explosion, scientists have two high cards to play in their one-upmanship game with the bug world. Also holding a trump or two are the researchers who suggest that new answers to pest control problems may lie in natural substances—found both in plants and other insects—that can induce harmful insects to keep their distance.

It is well known that some insects attack one crop with gusto but have little to do with the crop in the next field. Some chemical factor in the insect-free crop convinces the bug that he had better look elsewhere for his food. These natural resistance factors have been catalogued roughly into three general categories:

1. Volatile substances that the plant exudes into the atmosphere which actually repel the insect.
2. Materials which somehow interfere with the growth of the insect and limit its appetite for the host plant.
3. Chemical compounds that the insect just does not like when he bites into the plant.

Plant scientists are very interested in these natural resistance factors because it might be possible to isolate the substances, produce larger quantities and use them as chemical keep-off signs for harmful pests.

One natural resistance factor has been used as a bug

killer for centuries. Its name is nicotine, and just about everyone knows that it is produced in the tobacco plant. What is not known generally is that nicotine is manufactured only in the tobacco root, a discovery made by the German researcher, H. Huher. Dr. Huher proved his point when he grafted the upper part of a tobacco plant to a potato root. Without its normal root, the tobacco plant made no nicotine and was devoured by potato beetles. Conversely, Huher found that when a potato plant is grafted to a tobacco plant root, the beetle will not touch the potato plants.

Unfortunately, some insects, including the tobacco hornworm, can feed on tobacco plants with complete immunity. Apparently the normally poisonous nicotine moves through their systems before it can do any real damage.

Dr. Edward Smissman of the University of Kansas has recently found at least three natural resistance factors in corn plants, the most active of which affects a large number of insect types, including the wax moth larvae, the flour beetle, and most fortuitously, the corn borer.

Young corn plants seem to have large amounts of a resistance factor that decreases as they get older, according to the Kansas chemist. Apparently nature shows its consideration by giving the young plant all the resistance it needs when it is still vulnerable to insect attack. The adult plant, on the other hand, is still tough enough to withstand attack by the same insects. As added protection, the resistance factor concentrates in the most susceptible areas of the corn plant, that is, where the insect would normally lay its eggs.

Dr. Smissman hopes that isolation, purification and identification of the corn resistance factors might be of significant practical value to corn breeders attempting to develop insect-resistant varieties. Plant geneticists could run a quick chemical test to see if a young corn plant was a resistant variety instead of waiting for the results of extensive field trials.

Strangely enough, researchers at the Boll Weevil Research Laboratory in State College, Mississippi, report that the cotton plant has a split personality when it comes to resistance factors. It contains a natural substance that actually repels its age-old enemy, the boll weevil; but masking the effects of the repellent are:

1. A feeding stimulant that makes the plant tasty to weevils.

2. An attractant that lures the weevil to the boll.

Faced with these conflicting findings, the Mississippi researchers think that they might eventually be able to develop cotton plants that contain a maximum of resistance factors and a minimum of feeding stimulant, attractant, or both.

Some people do not think very much of turnips, parsnips and rutabagas as food, but many insects like them even less. Dr. E. P. Lichtenstein and his co-workers at the University of Wisconsin have isolated materials from all three vegetables that can kill a number of insect pests, including vinegar flies, Mexican bean beetles, mosquito larvae, houseflies and mites. There is also strong evidence that the roots of cabbages, cauliflower, Brussels sprouts, kale, mustard and kohlrabi have this same type of built-in protection against the insect world, says Dr. Lichtenstein.

The Wisconsin researcher believes that these natural

insecticides must be quite safe for man and animals, since they have been eaten for centuries without any obvious bad effects.

"Such chemicals might be of further importance in naturally protecting the edible portions of certain crops from insect attack, thus reducing the necessity for applied methods of insect control," the chemist points out.

The parsnip material—called myristicin—in addition to being as powerful as some current man-made insecticides—also is able to increase the killing power of several commercial bug-killers.

### REPELLENTS FOR PEOPLE

Since World War II, when American fighting men first became involved in large-scale jungle warfare, the USDA and the Department of the Army have been looking for chemicals that could be sprayed on the soldier's skin or uniform to ward off some of the most obnoxious jungle insects, including mosquitoes, tsetse flies, ticks, chiggers and fleas.

Dr. Carroll Smith of the USDA's Insects Affecting Animal and Man Laboratory in Gainesville, estimates that he and his colleagues have evaluated more than 13,000 different chemicals since World War II. One, called deet, or N, N-diethyl toluamide, proved so effective that it is now the active ingredient in commercial insect repellents found on most supermarket shelves. Deet works well in most climates, having been tested successfully from Alaska to Panama and throughout the continental United States.

One shortcoming of most chemical repellents is that they protect only the skin areas to which they have been applied, leaving exposed areas completely vulnerable to insect attack. And when the repellent wearer is as active as a G.I., it tends to get wiped off or rubbed away quite easily. Army researchers would be pleased if they could develop a repellent pill that would protect the wearer literally from the inside out, eliminating all the disadvantages of conventional spray or rub-on repellents.

Since 1960, scientists at the Army's Medical Research and Development Command have been scanning the world's scientific literature for pertinent clues to substances that might be used in a repellent pill. So far, they have a long list of drugs that, after being taken by mouth, appeared either in the skin or in perspiration. This didn't mean that they would be good insect repellents but it did give chemists ideas about related substances that would do the intended job.

Taking another tack, the Army scientists have been looking for people who are naturally repellent to insects because of some unknown factor in their constitutions. In fact, one investigator reports that most human beings contain fatty substances in their skin which are repellent to at least one species of mosquitoes. What these materials might be is still unknown; no one has yet been able to isolate or identify them.

### PARASITES AND PREDATORS

It is difficult to believe that before the white man came, North America was almost completely free of harmful crop pests. That may seem like a fairly obvious statement since—except for his success with corn—the American Indian was not much of a farmer. But there is more to it than that. The truth is that most of this country's major crop-destroying insects were introduced from other countries—principally European—as unwelcome by-products of America's increasing international trade. In most cases, when the insect invaders arrived, they turned out to be bigger pests than they ever were at home. Unfortunately they had left their natural parasites and predators behind.

By entomological definition, an insect predator preys on one or more insect species which it requires for its own growth and development. While predators feed on many insects, all parasites live in a single insect, feeding on it, until the parasite reaches another stage in its development. For example, a coccinellid larva will eat dozens of aphids before it reaches full development, while a parasite larva will consume only one host larva of the oriental fruit moth, codling moth or Japanese beetle.

For nearly eighty years, the United States Department of Agriculture has been making game, sometimes successful, often fruitless attempts to stock the countryside with parasites and predators from foreign countries that, it is hoped, will eliminate these accidentally introduced crop pests. In 1888, the department sent one Albert Koebele to hunt down some natural enemies of the "cottony cushion scale," a pest that nearly wiped out the California citrus industry of the time. Koebele came back to the States with a stock of 514 ladybird beetles that took to the California climate with great enthusiasm. Within two years, the cottony cushion scale was under control and it remains under control to this day.

Most of the insect parasites and predators brought to this country pass through the USDA's Insect Identification and Parasite Introduction Research Branch in Moorestown, New Jersey, and some are introduced directly by the California Department of Agriculture. After the insect immigrants are searched for evidences of parasites of their own, which are then eliminated, they are sent off to other parts of the country where they might be useful.

Getting a foreign predator to take hold in the different parts of the United States is not always an easy task, says Marvin H. Brunson, research director of the Moorestown station. Many beneficial insects that thrive in foreign countries may not survive when released in North America. For instance, some are so sensitive to slight changes in environment, or what Mr. Brunson calls "microclimates," that they will enjoy life in southern New Jersey, but will not last a season in the northern part of the state.

The evil perpetrated by the boll weevil has made him infamous in cotton-growing areas, but one of his cousins is becoming just as unpopular in other agricultural fields. Within the past fifteen years, the alfalfa weevil has graduated from a small-time Western pest to the most destructive forage pest in the East.

Entomologists at the Moorestown lab are now pinning their hopes on a number of weevil-destroying wasps, both domestic and imported. One such wasp, known as *Bathyplectes curculionis,* comes to the East Coast alfalfa fields via California, after being brought in from Italy. It is now one of several parasites making inroads into the alfalfa weevil population.

The imported wasp is more of a parasite than a true predator because it lays its eggs on the weevil's larvae. When the eggs hatch, the wasp larvae feed on the weevil larvae and kill them. Six members of the wasp family are now being brought into action as the alfalfa weevil extends its field of operations; five of these were introduced from Europe, and one is a native species that accepted the alfalfa weevil as a host after its arrival in the East.

As a federal organization, the USDA entomologists are likely to hear pleas for help from any of the fifty states. Recently Hawaiian sugarcane growers complained that their crop was being overrun by mealybugs. Because sugarcane is converted directly into feed, widespread spraying with insecticides was out of the question.

In the meanwhile, word had arrived from the Caribbean that sugarcane fields in the British island of Barbados were almost mealybug-free. The reason for the fortuitous mealybug shortage in Barbados—which has a climate similar to Hawaii's—is a type of lady beetle, or ladybug, known more specifically as *Hyperaspis trilineata*.

Adult ladybugs have an almost insatiable appetite for mealybugs in all stages, adult and larval. Apparently the taste develops early, because ladybug larvae steal the eggs right out from under the mother mealybug.

In 1963, Leon Coles left Moorestown to scour Barbados for ladybugs, collecting a grand total of 4,000. These were brought back to the New Jersey laboratories, checked out and sent on to Hawaii. At last report, they were still living as high on the mealybug as they ever did in Barbados.

Most entomologists will admit the need for chemical bug-killers, adding at the same time that the unwise use of pesticides has made their approach to insect control a harder job than it might ordinarily be. The success of a chemical spray attack on insects can often be evaluated overnight, but its effects must be tempered with the realization that some useful insects may also have been destroyed. Wide use of pesticides, says the USDA's Mr. Brunson, reduces the population of parasites and their beneficial insects. Under the best conditions, it may take from fifteen to twenty years for new parasite and predator populations to be introduced and built up to a point where they again control the insect pest.

Meeting both approaches halfway, Mr. Brunson believes that if insecticides are sprayed in the right amounts at the right time of year, they could leave the useful insects undisturbed.

### POSTSCRIPT

Research is not a static thing. Objectives are never fully met. As each frontier is crossed, another waits beyond, perhaps more exciting or more ominous than the last. Because man wants the best for himself, he tends to take the quickest route to assure his continued welfare. The auto is faster than the bicycle, and it is a major contributor to air pollution. Atomic energy can fill the power gap created by the depletion of traditional fuel resources, but it can destroy the world. Closer to the point, man develops insecticides to fight disease, create bigger crop yields, feed more people and enrich himself, but finds that they create new problems of their own.

It is not until long after he has crossed a research threshold that man is able to stand back and ask himself, "Did I really accomplish what I set out to accomplish?" Invariably, the answer must be, "Yes . . . but" or "No . . . but."

For a true researcher the "but" is the important word, signifying the unsatisfied urge to confront new problems and find new answers. Everything that has ever happened in the history of scientific research assures us that as certainly as the problems are there, so are the answers.

# A SELECTED BIBLIOGRAPHY

# A SELECTED BIBLIOGRAPHY

CHAPTER 1: THE PROTEIN GAP

Akroyd, W., *Food for Man*, London: Pergamon Press Ltd., 1964.

Albanese, A. A. (ed.), *Protein and Amino Acid Nutrition*, New York: Academic Press, Inc., 1959.

Allison, J. B., *Dietary Proteins in Health and Disease*, Springfield, Ill.: Charles C. Thomas, 1960.

Altschul, A. M. (ed.), *Processed Plant Protein Foodstuffs*, New York: Academic Press, Inc., 1958.

——, *Proteins, Their Chemistry and Politics*, New York: Basic Books, Inc., 1965.

Bennett, M. K., *The World's Food*, New York: Harper & Brothers, 1954.

Boyd Orr, Lord John, *Feast and Famine*, London: Rathbone, 1957.

Brock, J. F., *Recent Advances in Human Nutrition*, London: J. & A. Churchill Ltd., 1961.

May, J. M. and Jarcho, J. S., *The Ecology of Malnutrition in the Far and Near East*, New York: Hafner Publishing Co., Inc., 1961.

CHAPTER 2: MOLECULAR MEDICINE

Children's Bureau, United States Department of Health, Education and Welfare, *The Clinical Team Looks at Phenylketonuria*, Washington, D.C.: U.S. Government Printing Office, 1964.

Ingle, Dwight J., *Life and Disease*, New York: Basic Books, Inc., 1963.

Jervis, G. A., *Effect of Pharmacologic Agents on the Nervous System*, Baltimore: The Williams & Wilkins Co., 1959.

Joliffe, N. (ed.), *Chemical Nutrition*, (2nd ed.), New York: Harper & Brothers, 1962.

Lyman, Frank L. (ed.), *Phenylketonuria*, Springfield, Ill.: Charles C. Thomas, 1963.

McElroy, W. D. and Glass, B. (eds.), *A Symposium on the Chemical Basis of Heredity*, Baltimore: Johns Hopkins Press, 1957.

Penrose, L. S., *The Biology of Mental Defect*, London: Sidgwick & Jackson, 1949.

Rostand, J., *Can Man Be Modified?*, New York: Basic Books, Inc., 1959.

Wolstenholme, G. (ed.), *Man and His Future*, Boston: Little, Brown & Co., 1963.

## CHAPTER 3: DARWIN'S WARM LITTLE POND

Alexander, J., *Life, Its Nature and Origin*, New York: Reinhold Publishing Corp., 1947.

Asimov, Isaac, *Marvels of Science*, New York: Collier Books, 1962.

Bates, D. R., *The Earth and Its Atmosphere*, New York: Basic Books, Inc., 1957.

Bernal, J. D., *The Physical Basis of Life*, London: Routledge & Kegan Paul, Ltd., 1951.

Blum, H. F., *Time's Arrow and Evolution*, Princeton, New Jersey: Princeton University Press, 1955.

Calvin, M., *Chemical Evolution*, Eugene: University of Oregon Press, 1961.

Cameron, A. G. W. (ed.), *Interstellar Communication*, New York: W. A. Benjamin, Inc., 1963.

Clark, F. and Synge, R. L. M. (eds.), *The Origin of Life on Earth*, New York: Pergamon Press, Inc., 1959.

Davillier, A., *The Photochemical Origin of Life*, New York: Academic Press, Inc., 1965.

Ehrensvärd, Gösta, *Life: Origin and Development*, Chicago: University of Chicago Press, 1963.

Florkin, M., *Aspects of the Origin of Life*, New York: Pergamon Press, Inc., 1960.

Fox, Sidney (ed.), *The Origins of Prebiological Systems*, New York: Academic Press, Inc., 1965.

Keosian, John, *The Origin of Life*, New York: Reinhold Publishing Corp., 1964.

Oparin, A. I., *The Origin of Life*, New York: Dover Publications, Inc.

———, *Life: Its Nature, Origin and Development*, New York: Academic Press, Inc., 1964.

Sullivan, Walter, *We Are Not Alone*, New York: McGraw-Hill Book Co., Inc., 1964.

Urey, H. C., *The Planets*, New Haven: Yale University Press, 1952.

Young, Louise B., *The Mystery of Matter*, New York: Oxford University Press, 1965.

Young, R. S. and Ponnamperuma, Cyril, *Early Evolution of Life*, BSCS Pamphlet #11, Boston: American Institute of Biological Sciences, 1964.

CHAPTER 4: CHEMICAL FOOTPRINTS ON THE EVOLUTIONARY TRAIL

Anfinsen, Christian B., *The Molecular Basis of Evolution*, New York: John Wiley & Sons, Inc., 1963.

Asimov, Isaac, *The Wellsprings of Life*, New York: Abelard-Schuman, Limited, 1960.

Barry, J. M., *Molecular Biology, Genes and the Chemical Control of Living Cells*, Englewood Cliffs, N. J.: Prentice-Hall, Inc., 1964.

Beadle, George and Muriel, *The Language of Life*, New York: Doubleday & Company, Inc., 1966.

Borek, Ernest, *The Code of Life*, New York: Columbia University Press, 1965.

Dobzhansky, Theodosius, *Genetics and the Origin of the Species*, New York: Columbia University Press, 1964.

Ingram, V. M., *The Biosynthesis of Macromolecules*, New York: W. A. Benjamin, Inc., 1965.

——, *The Hemoglobins in Genetics and Evolution*, New York: Columbia University Press, 1963.

Tax, S. (ed.), *Evolution After Darwin*, Chicago: University of Chicago Press, 1960.

CHAPTER 5: THE WEB-BUILDING MACHINE

Comstock, John Henry, *The Spider Book*, Ithaca, N. Y.: Cornell University Press, 1965.

CHAPTER 6: SEARCH FOR A MEMORY MOLECULE

Adrian, E. D., *Physical Background of Perception*, Oxford: Oxford University Press, 1947.

Asimov, Isaac, *The Human Brain*, New York: New American Library, 1963.

Brachet, J. and Mirsky, A. E. (eds.), *The Cell*, Vol. 4, New York: Academic Press, Inc., 1960.

Brazier, M. A. B. (ed.), *Brain Function*, Vol. II, *RNA and Brain Function, Memory and Learning*, Berkeley: University of California Press, 1964.

Butler, J. A. V., *Inside the Living Cell*, New York: Basic Books, Inc., 1959.

Eccles, J. C., *The Neurophysiological Basis of Mind*, Oxford: Oxford University Press, 1953.

Eiduson, S., Geller, E., Yuwiler, A., and Eiduson, B., *Biochemistry and Behavior*, Princeton, N. J.: D. Van Nostrand Co., Inc.

Farber, S. M. and Wilson, R. H. L. (eds.), *Control of the Mind*, New York: McGraw-Hill Book Co., Inc., 1962.

Gaito, John (ed.), *Macromolecules and Behavior*, New York: Appleton-Century-Crofts, 1966.

Hebb, D. O., *The Organization of Behavior*, New York: John Wiley & Sons, Inc., 1949.

Hess, Walter Rudolf, *The Biology of Mind,* Chicago: University of Chicago Press, 1964.

Pfeiffer, John, *The Human Brain,* New York: Pyramid Publications, Inc., 1962.

Thorndike, E. L., *Human Learning,* Cambridge: Massachusetts Institute of Technology Press, 1966.

Walter, W. Grey, *The Living Brain,* New York: W. W. Norton & Company, Inc., 1955.

CHAPTER 9: HOW OLD IS IT?

Ahrens, Louis H., *Distribution of the Elements in Our Planet,* New York: McGraw-Hill Book Co., Inc., 1966.

Carrington, Richard, *A Guide to Earth History,* New York: New American Library, 1956.

Coon, Carleton S., *The Origin of Races,* New York: Alfred A. Knopf, Inc., 1962.

Faul, H. (ed.), *Nuclear Geology,* New York: John Wiley & Sons, Inc.

Hurley, Patrick M., *How Old Is the Earth?,* Garden City, N. Y.: Anchor Books, Doubleday & Company, Inc., 1959.

Le Gros Clark, W. E., *The Fossil Evidence for Human Evolution,* Chicago: University of Chicago Press, 1964.

Libby, Willard, *Radiocarbon Dating,* Chicago: University of Chicago Press, 1965.

Mason, Brian, *Principles of Geochemistry,* New York: John Wiley & Sons, Inc., 1962.

Rutten, M. G., *The Geological Aspects of the Origin of Life on Earth,* New York: American Elsevier Publishing Co., Inc., 1962.

Wendt, Herbert, *The Road to Man,* New York: Pyramid Publications, Inc., 1962.

CHAPTER 10: VIRUS KILLERS

Corbett, M. K. and Sisler, H. D., *Plant Virology,* Gainesville, Fla.: University of Florida Press, 1964.

Curtis, Helena, *The Viruses,* Garden City, N. Y.: Doubleday & Co., Inc., 1966.

Fraenkel-Conrat, H., *Design and Function at the Threshold of Life, The Viruses,* New York: Academic Press, Inc., 1962.

Stanley, Wendell M. and Valens, Evans, G., *Viruses and the Nature of Life,* New York: E. P. Dutton & Co., Inc., 1965.

Weidel, Wolfhard, *Virus,* Ann Arbor: University of Michigan Press, 1959.


CHAPTER 11: BATTLE ON THE BUG FRONT

Brown, A. W. A., *Insect Control by Chemicals,* New York: John Wiley & Sons, Inc., 1951.

Carson, Rachel, *Silent Spring,* New York: Houghton Mifflin Company, 1962.

De Bach, Paul and Schlinger, Evert I., *The Biological Control of Insect Pests,* New York: Reinhold Publishing Corp., 1964.

de Ong, E. R., *Chemical and Natural Control of Pests,* New York: Reinhold Publishing Corp., 1960.

———, *Chemistry and Use of Pesticides,* New York: Reinhold Publishing Corp., 1956.

Dethier, V. C., *Chemical Insect Attractants and Repellents,* Philadelphia: The Blakiston Co., 1947.

Elton, Charles S., *The Ecology of Invasions by Animals and Plants,* New York: John Wiley & Sons, Inc., 1958.

Gunther, F. A. and Jepson, L. R., *Modern Insecticides and World Food Production,* New York: John Wiley & Sons, Inc., 1960.

Jacobson, Martin, *Insect Sex Attractants,* New York: John Wiley & Sons, Inc., 1965.

McMillen, Wheeler, *Bugs or People?,* Des Moines, Iowa: Meredith Press, 1966.

Rudd, Robert L., *Pesticides and the Living Landscape,* Madison: University of Wisconsin Press, 1964.

# INDEX

245